Analyzing Statistics through Critical Thinking and Values

By Drs. Siamack Bondari and Jacci White
Saint Leo University

Analyzing Statistics through Critical Thinking and Values

Preface

To practice skills, go to the electronic resource, to think about statistics, read on...

Free throw percentage, RBI average, school grades, unemployment rates, mutual fund average performance numbers. Statistics are all around us. Are they always accurate? Are they intentionally biased? Do they unintentionally hurt anyone? Are they used to make better decisions? Are they abused to push through decisions? Even if Statisticians could agree on a common set of values to use in decision making, they couldn't be branded upon by all new people that enter the field. We believe that experience looking at the impact statistical results can have when they are publicized is as important as understanding how they were calculated and who was involved in the work. We also believe that every person needs to be able to think critically about not only their findings, but also about results obtained by others. This book attempts to summarize basic statistical calculations and then provide opportunities to explore findings and beliefs about those findings to bring into focus the set of values by which you already live and use them to think critically about a problem, in order to make wise decisions.

Contents

Chapter 1: Introduction to Statistics

In this section we will explore the terminology of Statistics including types of data, critical thinking, and the design of experiments.

Introduction and Definitions

Statistics: is the science of collecting, organizing, summarizing, describing, and interpreting data. The two types of statistics are:
- descriptive where data is used to describe a sample
- inferential where sample data is used to make predictions about a population

Example: suppose we give a quiz to a group of statistics students. We grade the quiz. The scores are as follows: 97, 83, 48, 73, 64, 91, 84, 85, and 88.

We have collected the data, but raw data is often hard to make conclusions from, so we use technology to organize the data by putting the scores in order from highest to lowest: 97, 91, 88, 85, 84, 83, 73, 64, 48.

We also compute the mean of the data, which is the sum of the scores divided by the number of students who took the quiz, 713/9 or approximately 79.22. Now we are ready to interpret the data and make conclusions by assigning letter grades to each score. Furthermore, based on the distribution of the scores and the mean, the test appears to be fair. Now we can predict that there are students who are probably not doing their work, while a few others might need a tutor.

Terminology

Population: is the complete collection of all the elements that we are interested in.

Sample: is any subset of a population.

A data (singular) is the value associated with the property or characteristic of one element of the population. Data may be a number, a word, or a symbol.

Examples:
Characteristic of the population that we are interested in: Student's GPA
A data point: 3.5

Characteristic of the population that we are interested in: eye color of a student
A data point: brown

Characteristic of the population that we are interested in: Political party affiliation
A data point: Democrat

Experiment: is a planned activity performed to collect data.

Parameter: is a single numerical value summarizing all the data for an entire population.

Statistic: is a single numerical value summarizing all the data for a given sample.

Examples:
Population: the set of all members of the United States Senate
Sample: the set of all the members of the United States Senate who are at least 50 years of age

Population: the set of all adults in the state of Florida who are eligible to vote
Sample: the set of all adults in the state of Florida who are eligible to vote and are in favor of the non-smoking in the public law

Population: the set of all students at Saint Leo University
Sample: the set of all students at Saint Leo University enrolled in the Mathematics program

Parameter: the average GPA of all students at Saint Leo University

Statistic: the average GPA of all Mathematics majors at Saint Leo University

Applications of statistics:

In practice populations are often extremely large, and we do not have access to all the data in the population. An important application of statistics is to make inferences about some property or characteristic of a population based on the results obtained from a sample taken from the population.

Example: Predict the results of a future Presidential election by conducting a phone survey of 10,000 people who are eligible to vote.

No matter how hard we try, there is always a chance that the results from the sample may not accurately describe the properties of the population.   In order to avoid false results, we must make every effort to ensure that our sample is a random sample that represents the larger population.   Bias or convenient samples will often yield invalid conclusions.   For example, the average GPA of all the students enrolled in a senior level course at Saint Leo University will not be a good predictor of the average GPA of all students enrolled at Saint Leo University.

Clearly larger samples will result in more reliable conclusions if the sample is collected appropriately. However, our resources are often limited and we prefer to get by with the minimum sample size that would get the job done. The sample size dilemma is addressed in a later chapter.

Types of Data

Data can be categorized in several different ways. First, it might be quantitative or qualitative.

Quantitative: Arithmetic with the four basic operations makes sense and can be represented in numeric form.
Examples: Student's test score, age, etc.

Qualitative: The four basic arithmetic operations do not make sense. Values represent categories, so qualitative data is often called categorical data.
Examples: Color of eyes, postal zip codes

Remark: A quantitative data must be numeric. However, there are examples of qualitative data that are represented by numbers. For example, postal zip codes, social security numbers, and area codes are all examples of qualitative data that are represented numerically.

This book will focus primarily on quantitative data. Quantitative data can be broken down further into discrete and continuous data.

Discrete: There is space between values that data can assume. These are values that are usually counted and cannot be broken down further.

Examples: Test scores, shoe sizes, number of classes on our schedule

Continuous: There is no space between values that data can assume. These values are usually measured.

Examples: Height, weight, time you are in class, or amount of soda in your glass.

Levels of Measurement:

Data can also be broken down into levels of measurement. You might think of this as a ladder. You test each step of the ladder to see if the data can go higher. The criterion from the highest step of the ladder that is satisfied for a particular set of data is considered the level of measurement for that data. The lowest level of measurement or first step on the ladder is the nominal level of measurement.

Nominal level of measurement is data that can be put in groups that make sense such as favorite food or classes at school. These sets of data cannot be put in a meaningful order or they would go to the next step.

Example: Some data can be put in order, such as player jersey numbers, however, this order does not make sense with the type of data it represents, so player jersey numbers would stay on this first step as nominal level of measurement.

Ordinal level of measurement is the second step on the ladder, when the data can be put in a meaningful order such as survey responses of disagree, somewhat disagree, neutral, somewhat agree and agree. Movie ratings of 1 through 5 are an example of the ordinal level of measurement. Notice in these cases, although the order is clear and meaningful, the difference between any two values in the data set is not exact or else they would go to the next step.

Example: if someone rates a movie as a 4.5 and another movie as a 4, we do not know the exact difference between the two movies, only that they liked the 4.5 better than the 4 so those ranking fit the ordinal level of measurement. If we can determine the exact different between the rankings then we would step up to the Interval level of measurement.

Interval level of measurement is ordered data where the exact difference between two data points can be determined such as temperature. If you have a list of temperatures, you can put them in order and determine exactly how many degrees separate any two data points. However, notice that temperature does not have a natural starting point since temperatures can go below zero, and that temperatures do not follow a ratio relationship in the sense that a 60 degree day is not twice as warm as a 30 degree day. If temperature followed those rules, it would go up the last step on the ladder to the ratio level of measurement.

Ratio level of measurement is data that has a natural starting point and ratios hold true such as weights. If there is no weight, then the weight is 0, so 0 is where weight values start. Also, if something weighs 44 pounds, it is twice as heavy as something that weighs 22 pounds.

Example: If you have a grade for your test, it is the ordinal level of measurement because you know that an A is higher than a B, but you do not know exactly how far apart grades A and B are. If you instead have scores for your tests such as scores of 40 and 80, you can not only put them in order, but you can also determine that 40 is 40 points less than 80 and that the score of 80 is twice as good as the score of 40 because the scores follow the ratio level of measurement with the natural starting point of zero.

Critical Thinking

Whenever you review statistical results, or work with statistics, you need to think critically about several key ideas including source, context, sampling method, conclusions, and significance. Each of these can influence the validity of the study.

The **source** is the person or group responsible for the study. You should determine if they are objective or if there is a personal or professional interest in the outcome of the study that might lead to bias. Is there an incentive to distort the results by either the person conducting the study or the person or group funding the study? The context of the data takes into account the actual data such as where it came from, how and why it was collected. You should make sure you understand why the study was done and how it was done.

The **sampling method** is critical, because no matter how careful you are when analyzing the data; nothing can make the experiment valid if the data was collected in a way that is not representative of the group being studied. Hence, you must know and understand the purpose of the sampling method before accepting any results from a study.

The **conclusions** and **significance** go hand in hand. The conclusion should be precisely related to the study and not broader than the variable that was tested. The findings would also need to be significant enough that the results are statistically expected to occur if the study was repeated again. You can then go one step further to determine whether the results have any practical implications, so that they would also have practical significance rather than just statistical significance.

Design of Experiments

In the design of experiments, you need to be aware of certain pitfalls to avoid. These pitfalls might include biased graphs, claims of causation rather than correlation, conclusions based on bad or small samples, faulty question, among others.

Some **graphs** that express bias can have scales that do not start at zero, so they emphasize the top of a graph where the differences will appear larger. Sometimes people will use a particular picture for a graph because of the feelings it generates, such as pictures of money or smiley faces. Other times a graph might increase in area or volume rather than just a linear change, so this makes the new graph look much larger than the first when in fact the linear change was not nearly so drastic.

Unfortunately, it is common to hear researchers express the findings of a regression analysis as one variable **causing** a change in the other. When in fact, the only thing they actually tested was whether the two variables were **correlated** or not. For example, seniors in my statistics class fail at a higher rate than freshman. I might state that being a senior causes you to fail statistics, but that is not true. More likely, there is a third variable that causes the two variables to change together. Maybe the seniors are afraid of math and have put it off to the end while the freshmen who enroll in Statistics take it because they are good at it and like it.

There are many ways a survey might contain **faulty questions**. A question can be loaded with an expected response based on the way it is asked. It can be loaded based on who is asking the question since people might respond differently to their parent, friend, teacher, or unknown statistician. Even the order of variables within the question can impact the response.

Collecting too little data can result in findings that are not accurate for the population. However, a very large sample will be no more accurate unless it is collected in a way that results in a sample that is representative of the population it came from. For example, convenience sampling would not usually represent a whole population, it would only be representative of the people that were around at the time the sampling was done. There are several types of sampling that can lead to a representative sample.

A **random sample** is one that is chosen in such a way that every element in the population is equally likely to be chosen. A **simple random sample** is a type of random sample where you select a group of n elements rather than single elements. However, it is still important that each different possible group of n such items have an equal chance to be chosen.

If you work in manufacturing, you might prefer a **systematic sample**. In this type of sample, each k-th element is chosen. For example, a company might test every 100th item that comes off of the assembly line in order to make sure everything is working correctly on the assembly line.

Sometimes the population can be broken into groups before a sample is collected. If the statistician collects a random sample from each group, this is called a **stratified sample**. If instead, a few entire groups are randomly chosen and the whole groups are then included in the sample, it is called **cluster sampling**.

Finally, once you have your sampling method, there are 3 types of studies you might conduct. If you want to collect the data and conduct the study all at one time, it is called a **cross sectional study**. If you prefer to go back and look at historical records and collect data to learn from our past, then you would do a **retrospective study**. Finally, if you are interested in following a group to see how they change over time, so that you look at them now and then continue to monitor them as they progress through a program or stages, you are conducting a **prospective** or sometimes called a **longitudinal study**.

Explorations

Team Exercises in the News:

1. Review news sources to find two different studies that use two different sampling methods such as random sampling, systematic sampling, stratified sampling, or cluster sampling. For both studies, identify the type of study (cross sectional, prospective, or retrospective), type of sampling, population and sample, type of data (qualitative or quantitative and discrete or continuous), level of measurement of the data (nominal, ordinal, interval, or ratio), source of the study, and conclusions of the study. Finally, summarize whether people

should or should not accept the findings in the study and explain why.

2. Choose a question of interest with an answer that is unknown to your team members. Work together to construct a study that could be used to attempt to answer your question. Be sure to indicate the type of study (cross sectional, prospective, or retrospective), type of sampling method (random, systematic, stratified, or cluster), population and sample, parameter and statistic, type of data (qualitative or quantitative and discrete or continuous), and the level of measurement of the data (nominal, ordinal, interval, or ratio). Note that you will not conduct the study, just set up the structure for the study based on the concepts in this chapter.

Values and Critical Thinking for Problem Solving:

1. Why is it important that a sample be representative of the population it came from?
2. Use any news source to find an example of a study or graph that is deceptive and explain why you believe it is deceptive and what should have been done differently.
3. If a study showed that many Business majors drop out of school immediately after

taking a Statistics class, what is wrong with the following statement? "A study indicates that the course requirement to take Statistics causes many Business majors to drop out of school." What are other possible lines of reasoning that might be true rather than Statistics causing people to drop out of school? What might be a correct interpretation of the study?

Writing across the Curriculum:

1. Write a short essay that can be used to teach someone how to determine the level of measurement of a given data set.

2. Choose any topic, such as basketball. Give an example of something related to that topic that could be studied as a cross sectional study such as determining the rankings for highest free-throw percentages. Give an example of a retrospective study related to that topic such as how the number of concussions in basketball over the last 5 years compares to other sports. Finally, give an example of a prospective study on the same topic such as following a group of 100 students who played basketball in high school to compare their bone density in their 20s, 30s, 40s, and 50s to those who did not play any sports.

3. Write a short summary that describes pitfalls to be aware of when reading statistical studies. Be sure to include examples.

Social Justice across the Curriculum:

For each of these questions, consider how the value of Respect relates to the situation and the importance of respect when conducting a statistical study.

1. Our national debt can be found in many different sources with the statistics represented many different ways. Identify three or more of these sources and discuss whether any of them provide a plan for the future generations to be able to pay for our spending.
2. What are your views on the country spending more money than it takes in? Support your views with statistical reports or documentation.
3. An "incentive" is often used to encourage people to participate in a study, such as free tickets to an event, money donated to a charity, a chance to win a prize, or even cash. How can an incentive create bias within the study? What group might likely not be included in a study and what group

might be over represented when an incentive is used?

Chapter 2: Summarizing and Graphing Data

Frequency distribution tables, graphs, and plots are used to organize, summarize, and describe the data. In this chapter we will cover frequency tables and various types of graphs and plots.

Frequency Distribution Tables

Data obtained from an experiment can be cumbersome and difficult to comprehend. A Frequency distribution table is often used to summarize and organize the data.

A <u>frequency distribution table</u> is a table that associates each value or class of values of the data to its frequency, the number of times the value occurs. The two types of frequency distribution tables are grouped and ungrouped frequency distribution tables.

<u>Example</u> of an ungrouped frequency table:

Data	Frequency
10	2
20	6
30	10
40	2

Note that in the above example there are n = 2+6+10+2 = 20 numbers in the data set.

Example of a grouped frequency table:

Data	Frequency
1-10	2
11-20	6
21-30	10
31-40	2

Definitions Related to Grouped Frequency Distributions

There are several definitions that relate to grouped frequency distributions. The left column in a frequency distribution is referred to as the classes or groups of data while the right side represents the frequencies, or the number of times each data value occurs in each class of the data set.

For each class, there are **lower** and **upper class limits**. The lower class limit is the left side value for each class, while the upper class limit is the right side of each class.

Between classes we have something called **class boundaries**. This is the halfway point between the upper limit of one class and the lower limit of the next class. It is referred to as the upper boundary of one class and the lower boundary of the next class. In order to find the lower boundary of the first class, find the difference between the upper limit and the upper boundary of the first class and then subtract this value from the lower limit of the first class. In order to find the upper boundary of the last class, find the difference between the lower limit and lower boundary of the last class and then add this value to the upper limit of the last class.

Class midpoints are the midpoints for each class and can be found by adding the lower and upper class limits of a class and then dividing by two.

Finally, the **class width** is the distance between any two consecutive lower class limits, or any two consecutive upper class limits.

Example:

Data	Frequency
0-99	5
100-199	8
200-299	13
300-399	12
400-499	19

Lower class limits, 0, 100, 200, 300, 400
Upper class limits: 99, 199, 299, 399, and 499

Class boundaries: -0.5, 99.5, 199.5, 299.5, 399.5, 499.5
Class midpoints: 49.5, 149.5, 249.5, 349.5, 449.5
Class width: 100

Constructing a Frequency Table

When constructing a frequency table, you should look at the size of your data set and select between 5 and 20 classes, remembering that you want to break into only enough groups to recognize patterns in the data. Fifteen to twenty classes are usually only used in cases of extremely large data sets. Then, look at the range of your data set and divide that by the number of classes that you selected. Take your result and round up to the next integer to get your class width. If you mistakenly round down, your last class might end before you get to your last data point, although you can always add another class. As long as you include all the data, you can have a few more or less classes than you originally planned, so you should feel free to round slightly higher or slightly lower. This flexibility might allow you to choose a more convenient class width such as 5 rather than 6, or 10 rather than 8.

In starting your first class, you should look for a convenient number that is at or below your first data point. For example, if your data point is either 10, 11, 12, 13, or 14, it might be convenient for you to start your first class at 10 because that is a nice round number to work with. Then, add the class width to get the next lower class limit. Once all the lower class limits have been filled in, you would choose the upper class limit as the closest value to the next lower class limit. For example, if your lower class limits are 10, 20, 30, ... then your upper class limits would be 19, 29, 39, ... While if your lower class limits are 25.0, 30.0, 35.0, ... Then your upper class limits might be 29.9, 34.9, 39.9, ... Continue until your classes are determined.

Now you are ready to fill in the frequency for each class. The class frequency for a class is the total number of data points that fall within the boundaries of that class. You find this number by counting the data points within each range and then record that number on the right side column of the frequency table.

Example: Given the data below, construct a frequency table.
6, 8, 9, 11, 7, 3, 3, 5, 9, 10, 12, 0, 4, 10, 7, 6, 8, 9, 4, 5, 13, 1, 4, 4, 5, 3, 6, 9, 2, 3, 4, 8, 10, 9, 7, 6, 2, 6, 11, 1, 4, 5, 8, 7, 6, 3, 8, 9, 10, 7, 7, 7, 10, 6, 8

Solution: There are 55 data points that range from 0 to 13. This is a rather small data set so I will go with 5 classes. Furthermore, since 15 is divisible by 5 classes, I will go from 0 to 14 (15 units) and with 5 classes that makes each class 3 units wide.

My lower class limits will be 0, 3, 6, 9, and 12; so my upper class limits must be 2, 5, 8, 11, and 14.
Frequency table:

Data	Frequency
0-2	5
3-5	15
6-8	20
9-11	13
12-14	2

Total:55

Relative Frequency Distribution Tables

In a relative frequency distribution table, frequency of each class is replaced by its relative frequency, or proportion, or percentage of data that falls within that class.

Relative frequency = class frequency / sum of all frequencies

Example: Start with the frequency table, then divide the frequency of each class by the total number of data points in the entire table.

Frequency table:

Data	Frequency
0-2	5
3-5	15
6-8	20
9-11	13

12-14	2

Total: 55

Relative frequency table:

Data	Relative Frequency
0-2	5/55=9.09%
3-5	15/55=27.27%
6-8	20/55=36.36%
9-11	13/55=23.64%
12-14	2/55=3.64%

Total: 100%

Due to round off, sometimes the sum of the relative frequencies may add up to a number slightly different from 100%.

Pay close attention to the relative frequency distribution because it is very similar to the probability distribution found in the probability chapter.

Cumulative Frequency Tables

The last type of frequency distribution we will explore in this section is the cumulative frequency distribution. Just like a cumulative exam, a cumulative frequency distribution includes all current data as well as all data that came before. You find the cumulative frequency for each class by adding the frequency from that class and all previous classes.

Example: Construct a cumulative frequency table for the example from the previous page.

Data	Cumulative Frequency
0-2	5
0-5	5+15 = 20
0-8	20+20 = 40
0-11	40+13= 53
0-14	53+2 = 55

Notice that the final cumulative frequency should be the total number of data points in the set since it is the sum of all data points in the distribution.

Organizing Data Using Graphs and Plots

Histograms

A histogram is a bar graph in which the height of each bar represents the frequency of each class of data. Similarly in a relative frequency histogram height of each bar represents the relative frequency of each class.

In histograms, you can use either the class limits or the class boundaries to label the classes along the horizontal axis.

Example: Construct a histogram and a relative frequency histogram for the following frequency distribution table.

Data	frequency	Relative frequency
0-2	5	9.09%
3-5	15	27.27%
6-8	20	36.36%
9-11	13	23.64%
12-14	2	3.64%

There are 5 classes, so there will be 5 bars in the histogram. Notice there are no breaks between the bars in a histogram because this graph can be used for continuous as well as discrete data. A bar graph can replace a histogram for discrete data since breaks between the bars are fine in that situation.

Frequency Histogram

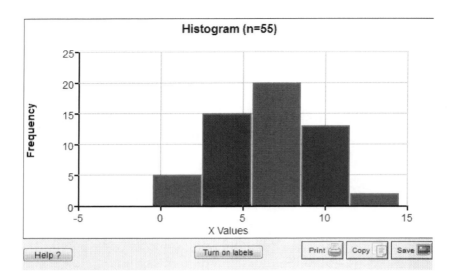

Relative Frequency Histogram

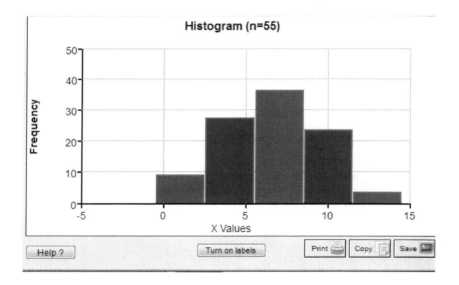

Dot Plots

In a dot plot each value of data is represented by a dot on a number line above the value that corresponds to the data point. If there is already a dot, then the new dot goes above the dot that already exists for that value. Common values appear as higher areas of the dot plot while less common areas are lower or have no dots at all.

The dot plot is one of only a few types of graphs that retain the original value of every data point so that the plot could be used to reconstruct the original set of data. In most graphs the data is first organized into a grouped frequency distribution and then graphed so only frequency of classes can be determined, not the original data values.

Example: Construct a dot plot for the following frequency distribution table.

Data	Frequency
1	1
2	4
3	3
4	2

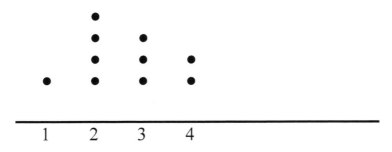

Pie Charts

In a pie chart each slice represents a class of data. The relative frequency distribution is often used for a Pie Chart because each slice of the pie represents the proportion of data in that class. For example, if one class contains 25% of the data, then the corresponding slice of pie will be ¼ or 25% of the pie.

Example: Construct a Pie chart of the following data.

Data	frequency	Relative frequency
0-2	5	9.09%
3-5	15	27.27%
6-8	20	36.36%
9-11	13	23.64%
12-14	2	3.64%

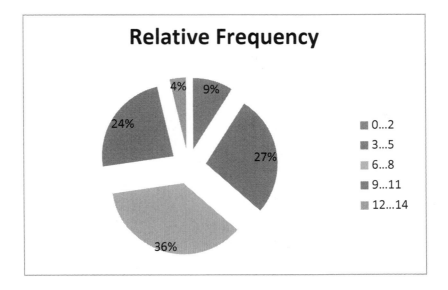

Relative Frequency

- 0...2
- 3...5
- 6...8
- 9...11
- 12...14

Scatter Diagrams

A Scatter diagram is a plot of the paired (x, y) data with a horizontal x-axis and a vertical y-axis. This is a common type of plot used in regression analysis. This plot is usually used whenever data is arranged in ordered pairs. More information on the Scatter Diagram can be found in the chapter on Linear Regression.

Stem-and-leaf Plots

In a stem-leaf plot each data is represented by two parts: stem and leaf. The stem is often the first digit of each number while the leaf is made up of the remaining digits. The stem is listed once on the left side of the plot and then each number is expressed individual on the right side of the plot as the remaining leaf. The stem may occasionally contain more than one digit and the leaves are the remaining digits.

Example:

Data: 25, 26, 29, 30, 30, 35. 38, 45, 48, 48, 49

Stem and leaf plot:

Stem	Leaves
2	5 6 9
3	0 0 5 8
4	5 8 8 9

Graphing Summary:

The dot plot and stem and leaf plot are often used with small sets of data or especially when you want to retain the value of the original data. Histograms and Pie charts are a way to summarize larger sets of data when the individual points do not need to be retained.

When you are looking at scatter plots and histogram graphs, always check to be sure that the graphs start with a vertical axis value of zero. Sometimes a researcher will only include the top portion of the graph, starting their bar chart far above zero, in order to emphasize a difference that appears at the top of the graph. Other researchers might use pictures or colors to manipulate your emotions rather than focusing on the meaning of the data with the graph. Always look at what the graph is representing before allowing a researcher to use your emotions or reflexes to come to a conclusion that they intend but that may not be supported by the true nature of the data.

Explorations

Team Exercises in the News

1. Find an article that contains at least one statistical graph. Identify the original data as closely as possible from the information given in the study. Do this again for another study that has a different type of graph. In which study were you able to most closely determine the original data? Why? (if you cannot determine much about the original data, then you should find another study to work with)

2. Find a graph in an article. Each team member should create a different type of graph from the same information. Do the graphs appear to express the same results or give a different impression? Which graph is a good choice and why? Which graph is a bad choice and why?

Critical Thinking for Problem Solving:

1. Make up or find a set of data. Graph the set of data two ways that project two different meanings. Include a brief description of how the two graphs imply different meaning.
2. Find two different graphs for the same topic and explain how and why they are similar and different.
3. Find two different visual representations of the same information and explain why they are accurate or not accurate and how you might be able to express the same information in two different yet equally accurate ways.

Writing across the Curriculum about Values:

1. Explain why Integrity is important when reporting statistical findings.
2. Write a short summary that describes techniques to be aware of when interpreting statistical graphs so you are not fooled with bias graphs.
3. Find at least one study about something that interests you and explain what you learned from the study or studies.

Social Justice across the Curriculum

For each of these questions, consider how the value of Respect relates to the situation and the importance of respect when conducting a statistical study.

1. Find a study that you should be cautious in interpreting because it is sponsored by a group or organization that you believe might be biased on the issue being presented. Explain whether any bias is apparent within the study.
2. Find a study that can be interpreted in a way that could be harmful to a group in our society (this should be very difficult to find since one rule for any regulated research is that it will do no harm to animals or people)
3. Should authors be held accountable for bias reports? Why or why not? How?

Chapter 3: Measures of Center, Variation, and Relative Standing

Measures of center, variation, and relative standing (position) are used to gain valuable insight about important characteristics of data. In this chapter we shall investigate the major concepts associated with the measures mentioned above. The topics covered are as follows:

Measures of center: mean, median, mode, midrange
Measures of variation: range, standard deviation, variance
Measures of relative standing (position): Z-score, quartiles, percentiles Chebyshev's Rule, and the Empirical Rule, the Range Rule of Thumb.

Measures of Center

Measures of center are numerical values that provide us with information about the center of the data. These are mean, median, mode, and midrange.

Mean

The most important measure of center is mean of the data, which is denoted by $\bar{x}$ (x-bar). Mean of a set of data is simply the weighted average of the data.

$$\bar{x} = \frac{\sum x}{n} = (\text{sum of all the numbers in the}$$

data)/(number of values in the data)

Example: The scores in a Statistics quiz are: 97, 83, 48, 73, 64, 91, 84, 85, 88, and 22. Find the mean of the quiz.

Solution: $\bar{x} = \frac{\sum x}{n} =$

(97+83+48+73+64+91+84+85+88+22)/10 = 735/10 =73.5

The mean is the most common measure of center. It takes all the values of data and their weights into account. It is used in many areas of statistics. It can be pulled by an outlier, but not as heavily as some other measures of center since it utilizes all of the data to counter balance any one extreme value.

Median

The median $\tilde{x}$ (x-tilde) is the value of data that is located in the middle position, once the data is arranged in either ascending or descending order. The middle location is determined differently depending upon whether n, the total number of data points, is even or odd. If n is odd, then the median is the value in the center, once the data is ordered. If n is even, then the median is the average of the two values located at the center, once the data is ordered.

Example (n is odd): Find the median of the quiz scores 97, 83, 48, 73, 64, 91, 84, 85, and 88.

Solution: Sort the data: 97, 91, 88, 85, 84, 83, 73, 64, 48
Median = 84

Example (n is even): Find the median of the quiz scores 97, 83, 48, 73, 64, 91, 84, 85, 88, and 22.

Solution:
Sort the data: 97, 91, 88, 85, 84, 83, 73, 64, 48, 22
Median = (84+83)/2 = 83.5

The median is the second most common measure of center. The median is not affected by outliers at all, so it is often used in situations with extreme values such as average home prices or average salaries.

Mode

Mode is the value of the data that appears with the highest frequency.

<u>Example:</u> Data: 25, 55, 75, 75, 75, 85, 95   Mode: 75
<u>Example:</u> Data: 25, 55, 55, 55, 75, 75, 75, 85, 95
Modes: 55 and 75
<u>Example:</u> Data: 25, 55, 65, 75, 85, 95   Modes: none

<u>Bimodal:</u> If two values of the data share the same greatest frequency, the set of data is said to be bimodal and two modes would be listed.

<u>Multimodal:</u> If more than two values of the data share the same greatest frequency, then the set of data is said to be multimodal and no mode is listed.

Mode is only used as a measure of center either in conjunction with other measures of center, or when the most common data point is the objective.

Midrange

Midrange of a set of data is defined to be the average of the highest and lowest value, or the value half way between the highest and lowest data point.

(highest value of data+ lowest value of data) / 2.

The midrange is only used as a measure of center when the information about a set of data is limited or a very quick estimate is needed. The midrange is often a bias estimate of the center because it is heavily pulled in the direction of outliers since it is calculated using only the most extreme high and low values.

Example: Find the midrange of the Statistics quiz with scores: 97, 83, 48, 73, 64, 91, 84, 85, 88, and 22.

Solution: Midrange = (97+22)/2 = 119/2 = 59.5 Note that the midrange is well off from the mean=73.5.

Round-off Rule

A widely used round-off rule in statistics is to carry the computations one decimal place further than the number of decimal places present in the original set of data.

Mean of a Frequency Table

You should find that Statistics at this level is a very consistent science. For example, the round off rule above will repeat each time we apply the mean in other areas such as probability distributions in the future. In addition, the mean of a frequency distribution here will be the same calculation that is used to find the mean of a probability distribution in the future. Remember, the mean is simply the average of all values in the set of data. In the frequency distribution example below, the first line means there are 5 distinct values of 1 and 15 distinct values of 4 within the set of data. That means we can find the sum of all 5 values of 1 by multiplying the 5 times the 1. The same can be done by multiplying the 15 by 4 to find the value of all 15 of the data points of 4. The steps are shown below. Remember, if you add up the total frequency, that will give you the total number of values in your data set for your value of n.

Example: Find the mean of the following table.

Data	Frequency
1	5
4	15
7	20
10	13
13	2
	total =55

Solution: Mean = Sum(x) / n =
[(1)(5)+(4)(15)+(7)(20)+(10)(13)+(13)(2)]/55 =
361/55 or approximately 6.56

Example 2: Find the mean of the following table.

Data	Frequency
0-2	5

3-5	15
6-8	20
9-11	13
12-14	2

<u>Solution:</u> In this case, we do not know the actual values of the data points, only the range that each value falls within. As a result, the midpoint of each class is the best estimate of the values within that class. That means you should first convert the table to an ungrouped table by replacing each class of data by its class midpoint. In this example, the result will be identical to the table given in example 1. Then:

Mean = Sum(x) / n =
[(1)(5)+(4)(15)+(7)(20)+(10)(13)+(13)(2)]/55 =
361/55 or approximately 6.56

In order to calculate the mean of a grouped frequency distribution table, you first need to convert the grouped table to an ungrouped table by replacing each class of data by the midpoint of the class. The result will be an approximation.

Skewed Distributions

A distribution of data is skewed if it is not symmetric and extends more to one side than the other. For example, if it looks like someone pulled the left side of your distribution so it sticks out long and thin, then the data is skewed to the left and the mean and median are to the left of the mode. If it looks like you pulled the data on the right so that the right side is stretched thin, then the set is skewed to the right and the mean and median are to the right of the mode. If the distribution of data is symmetric and bell shaped, then it is not skewed, it is considered a normal distribution and the mean, median, and mode will be the same.

<u>Measures of Variation</u>

Consider the following sets of data.

Data set #1: 0, 10, 50, 90, 100
Data set #2: 45, 45, 50, 55, 55

The mean and the median for both sets of data is 50. Therefore, if we only take measures of center into account, there is no significant difference between the two data sets. However, it is obvious the two sets are very different. The numbers in the first set are spread out while the numbers in the second set are clustered in the middle. Measures of variation take spread of the data into consideration and provide us with more information about the data. In the next few pages, we will discuss measures of variation: range, variance, and standard deviation.

Range

The range of a set of data is defined to be the difference between the highest and lowest value in the data set

Range = highest value − lowest value.

This measure of spread is not used very often for the same reason the midrange is not popular, it is heavily skewed by extreme values.

Example: What is the range of the set: 45, 45, 50, 55, 55?
The highest value is 55 and the lowest value is 45 so the range is 55-45=10.

Variance and Standard Deviation of a Sample and a Population

We want to come up with a way to measure the spread of the data. To achieve this task, we must somehow include the deviation of each value x from the mean or $x - \bar{x}$ in our calculations. An obvious attempt would be to calculate the average of all the deviations from the mean or $\dfrac{\sum(x - \bar{x})}{n}$. Unfortunately the numerator, the sum of all the deviations $\sum(x - \bar{x})$ is always zero. This is because the mean is the average of all values so

47

they are equally spread above and below the mean so the positive and negative differences cancel each other out. In order to avoid a sum of zero, we will square all the deviations and then find the mean by dividing the sum by n-1. The result is called the <u>variance of the sample</u>.

Therefore for a given sample, we have:

$$\text{Variance of sample} = s^2 = \frac{\sum (x - \bar{x})^2}{n-1}$$

$$\text{Standard deviation of sample} = s = \sqrt{\frac{\sum (x - \bar{x})^2}{n-1}}$$

If the mean is computed by dividing by n, the results are referred to as the variance and the standard deviation of the population. Thus for a given population:

$$\text{Variance of population} = \sigma^2 = \frac{\sum (x - \bar{x})^2}{n}$$

$$\text{Standard deviation of population} =$$
$$\sigma = \sqrt{\frac{\sum (x - \bar{x})^2}{n}}$$

In life, we hardly ever have access to all the numbers in the population. Unless it is specifically stated that the numbers represent the entire population, you must use the sample formulas to obtain the variance and the standard deviation.

Example: Find the variance and the standard deviation of the sample data 45, 45, 50, 55, 55.

Solution:
Obviously n = 5 and mean = (45+45+50+55+55)/5 = 50
If we carry out the problem the long way, then we organize the information in a table. We strongly recommend that students should use technology to compute the standard deviation.

x	$x - \bar{x}$	$(x - \bar{x})^2$
45	-5	25
45	-5	25
50	0	0
55	5	25
55	5	25
		$\sum (x - \bar{x})^2 = 100$

Variance = $s^2 = \dfrac{\sum (x - \bar{x})^2}{n - 1}$ = 100 / 4 = 25

Standard deviation = $s = \sqrt{25} = 5$

This is an excellent time to get familiar with some form of technology if you have not already. It is impossible to calculate something as simple as standard deviation with some of the sources of data that contain millions of values these days.

If you are using Statdisk, you should enter all of the data into column 1. Then, select the "data" menu at the top and drop down to "explore data". When that window opens, select "evaluate" and you will see a list containing many features that describe the data set including: size, mean, median, range, variance, and standard deviation. We will use these same steps to create a box plot and 5 number summary soon. The result for the example above will look something like:

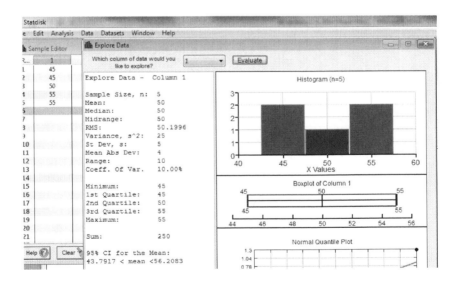

Other helpful technology might include Excel – using the "insert – function – statistical" menu options. Most financial and graphing calculators also have the basic statistical features we have looked at so far.

Example: Find the variance and the standard deviation of the sample data 0, 10, 50, 90, 100.

Solution:
Obviously n = 5 and mean = (0+10+50+90+100)/5
= 50

x	$x - \bar{x}$	$(x - \bar{x})^2$
0	-50	2500
10	-40	1600
50	0	0
90	40	1600
100	50	2500
		$\sum (x - \bar{x})^2 = 8200$

Variance = $s^2 = \dfrac{\sum (x - \bar{x})^2}{n - 1}$ = 8200 / 4 = 2050

Standard deviation = $\sqrt{2050} \propto 45.28$

As expected, the standard deviation is much larger than the standard deviation for the previous example.

Notation Summary

	Sample	Population
Mean	$\bar{x}$	μ
Variance	s^2	σ^2
Standard Deviation	s	σ

The Range Rule of Thumb

According to the Range Rule of Thumb, the standard deviation of a set of data is approximately the range divided by 4 or s = (range)/4.

Example: Use the Range Rule of Thumb to approximate the standard deviation of 0, 10, 50, 90, 100.

Solution: Range = 100-0=100.   Standard deviation is approximately 100/ 4 or 25.

Note that earlier we calculated the true standard deviation of the above set of data to be approximately 45.28, which is very different from the result obtained from the Range Rule of Thumb. The Range Rule of Thumb is a quick method to guess standard deviation of a set of data and the result may not be very accurate. Use this rule only if you do not have access to all the sample data or if you are specifically asked to do so.

The idea behind this rule is important as we shall learn later that approximately 95% of the data in a normal distribution falls within 2 standard deviations of the mean. This is also the way to determine if an outcome is unlikely. If a data is more than 2 standard deviations above or below the mean (outside the Range Rule of Thumb), then it is considered unusual. If the data is from a normal distribution, that means there is 5% chance that the result is unusual.

Chebyshev's Theorem

Chebyshev's Theorem: Let k>1. The proportion of any set of data lying within k standard deviations of the mean is always at least $1 - \dfrac{1}{k^2}$.

As stated earlier, in most distributions a vast majority of the data falls within 2 standard deviations of the mean. Even though Chebyshev's Theorem is valid for any positive number k>1, typically we apply the theorem only for k=2 and k=3.

k= 2: at least 3/4 (75%) of all values of data lie within 2 standard deviations of the mean.

k=3: at least 8/9 (89%) of all values of data lie within 3 standard deviations of the mean.

Example: The mean of an exam is 65 with a standard deviation of 8. Use Chebyshev's Theorem to determine the percentage of data within 2 and 3 standard deviations of the mean.

Solution: For k=2: 2 standard deviations will be (2)(8)=16. According to Chebyshev Theorem, at least 3/4 or 75% of all the scores fall between 65-16 and 65+16. In other words, at least 3/4 or 75% of the scores fall between 49 and 81.

For k=3: 3 standard deviation will be (3)(8)=24. According to Chebyshev Theorem, at least 8/9 or 89% of all the scores fall between 65-24 and 65+24. In other words, at least 8/9 or 89% of the scores fall between 41 and 89.

It is important to keep in mind that Chebyshev's Theorem is a very general and conservative theorem that applies to ANY distribution. If the distribution satisfies additional properties, then the percentages will increase. In real life application problems, we often work with symmetric bell shaped distributions known as normal distributions. If a distribution is normal, then Chebyshev's Theorem is replaced by the Empirical Rule.

Empirical Rule (or 68-95-99.7% Rule)

Empirical Rule or the 68-95-99.7% Rule applies only for data with a bell-shaped, symmetric distribution, known as a normal distribution

- Approximately 68% of all values fall within 1 standard deviation of the mean.
- Approximately 95% of all values fall within 2 standard deviations of the mean.
- Approximately 99.7% of all values fall within 3 standard deviations of the mean.

The Empirical Rule does not contradict the Chebyshev's Theorem. However, for normal distributions, the Empirical Rule provides us with much better results than the Chebyshev's Theorem.

Example: It is known that the IQ scores for a large population has a normal distribution with mean of 100 and standard deviation of 15. If we apply the Empirical Rule, we obtain the following results.

Roughly 68% of all the IQ scores are between 85 and 115.
Roughly 95% of all the IQ scores are between 70 and 130.
Roughly 99.7% of all the IQ scores are between 55 and 145.
Furthermore, the IQ scores less than 70 and greater than 130 are considered to be unusual.

Measures of Relative Standing (Position)

Measures of relative standing are used to describe the position of a specific value of the data in relation to the rest of the data. For example, how do schools determine the admission cut-off ACT and SAT scores since the values for those tests are on very different scales? Each can be compared to the mean of all students who took the tests and the relative standing can be compared even though the numeric values are very different.

Z Scores

The z-scores of a value x of data is a measure of the position of x in terms of mean and standard deviation of the distribution. In other words, the z-score represents how many standard deviations x is above or below the mean for that sample. This is found by taking the difference between a data point and the mean, and then dividing by the standard deviation.

z = (x- mean) / standard deviation

Sample notation: $z = \dfrac{x - \bar{x}}{s}$

Population notation: $z = \dfrac{x - \mu}{\sigma}$

z-score tells us how many standard deviations the x value of data is above or below the mean. A negative z-score means x is below the mean while a positive z-score means x is above the mean.

If the distribution is normal, then according to the Empirical Rule, roughly 68% of all the z scores are between -1 and +1, roughly 95% of all the z scores are between -2 and +2, and finally, approximately 99.7% of all the z scores are between -3 and +3. The x values, or data points, with z score less than -2 or greater than +2 are considered to be unusual.

Example: Use Empirical Rule to determine the percentage of the data that falls below a value of data with z score of (a) z = +1, and (b) z = +2 for a given bell shaped symmetric normal distribution.

Solution:
  (a) According to the Empirical Rule, approximately 68% of all z scores are between -1 and +1. Therefore, approximately 34% of all z scores are between 0 and +1. Since the distribution is bell shaped and symmetric, 50% of all the scores are below z = 0. Therefore, approximately (50+34)% or 84% of all the data have z scores less than z = +1.
  (b) We can use a similar approach to arrive at the conclusion that approximately (50+47.50)% or 97.5% of all the data have z scores less than z = +2.

The above example shows you how z score can be used to compare values of data from completely different normal distributions with different means and different standard deviation. Values of data with identical z score from different normal distributions have the exact same relative position. A value of data with a larger z score has a higher relative position. For example, a value of data with z = -1.4 has a higher relative position that a value of data with z = -1.8, and a value of data with z = 2.2 has a higher relative position than a value of data with z = 2.1.

Example: Jane received a score of 75 in her Finite Mathematics class. The mean for the exam was 65 and the standard deviation was 7. Krishnan received a score of 65 in his College Algebra class. The mean for the exam was 55 and the standard deviation was 8. Joe received a score of 70 in his Statistics class. The mean for the exam was 60 and the standard deviation was 6. Who got the highest relative score?

Solution: At the first glance, Jane appears to have the highest score. However, the means of the three exams are different. A second look reveals the fact that all three students earned 10 points above the class average. So who did better relative to his or her own class? We need to compute the z scores.

Jane's relative position $z = (75-65)/7 = 10/7$ or approximately 1.43

Krishnan's relative position $z = (65-55)/8 = 10/8 = 1.25$

Joe's relative position $z = (70-60)/6 = 10/6$ or approximately 1.67

Joe has the highest relative position. Joe did better on his test relative to his class than Jane and Krishnan did relative to their own classes.

Quartiles, Percentiles, and 5 number summary

A sample can be broken into segments separating certain percentages of the data. For example, quartiles break the sample data into 4 quarters while percentiles can break the data into 100 segments. Once the data is sorted in ascending order, we can define quartiles and percentiles as follows.

Quartile 1 = Q_1 = Separates the bottom 25% of the data from the top 75%.

Quartile 2 = Q_2 = median = Separates the bottom 50% of the data from the top 50%.

Quartile 3 = Q_3 = Separates the bottom 75% of the data from the top 75%.

Percentile $1 = P_1 =$ Separates the bottom 1% of the data from the top 99%.

Percentile $2 = P_2 =$ Separates the bottom 2% of the data from the top 98%.

...

Percentile $50 = P_{50} = Q_2 =$ median = Separates the bottom 50% of the data from the top 50%.

...

Percentile $82 = P_{82} =$ Separates the bottom 82% of the sorted values from the top 18%.

...

The 5 number summary of data gives a good picture of the data. In fact, the 5 number summary are the 5 values used to graph a sample using a box plot, sometimes called a box and whisker plot.

The 5 number summary begins with the lowest point in the sample, followed by the first, second, and third quartile, and finally the highest point in the sample. The three quartiles make up the box in the middle with Q_1 as the left side of the box, the Q_3 as the right side of the box and Q_2 as a small line down the center of the box. Now, stick a "whisker" out each side of the box that extends to the lowest value on the left and the highest value on the right.

Example: Explore the 5 number summary and box plot from a sample containing the values 1, 3, 5, 7, 9

Notice the data is listed in the column on the left. Then, "Data" was selected from the drop down menu in Statdisk followed by "explore data" and finally "evaluate." The 5 number summary is in the center starting with the "minimum" and finishing with the "maximum." The boxplot is located in the bottom right corner of the figure.

Explorations

Team Exercise in the News:

Saint Leo University is an educational enterprise. All of us, individually and collectively, work hard to ensure that our students develop the character, learn the skills and assimilate the knowledge essential to become morally responsible leaders. The success of our University depends upon a conscientious commitment to our mission, vision and goals. Saint Leo has used the phrase Points of Pride in reference to some of the results of this continuing commitment. A few of those points in the past have included:

- One of the largest providers of higher education to the military
- Ranked second in the nation in the number of bachelor's degrees in business awarded to African-American students
- One of the largest providers of higher education online
- Ranked as the third largest among private universities and colleges in Florida
- The largest of three Catholic institutions in Florida

- Ranked eighth in overall enrollment among Catholic colleges and universities

Break into teams, choose any of the "Points of Pride" for Saint Leo University, and back up or refute the statement using any effective combination of statistical graphs and data analysis tools. Yes, you will have to use the web to do some research.

Values and Critical Thinking for Problem Solving:

1. Does it Add Up: What's Your Grade?
A mean is an average. A weighted mean can occur when different values hold different weights in the final average. Choose sample scores for each one of your assignments in this class and calculate your final course grade using the idea of a weighted mean. Is a course grade something in which to take pride in? Can your effort in this course reflect the value of Excellence even though your grade may not?
2. What is a set of data that would have a skewed distribution and why is it skewed? Is there any bias as a result of the skewed nature of the data you found?

Writing across the Curriculum:

1. Compare and contrast mean, median, mode, and midrange. Be sure to explain the advantages and disadvantages of each.
2. Explain how a score of 68% on one test could possibly be considered better than a score of 85% on a different test using the idea of relative standing.

Social Justice across the Curriculum:

1. Why is the median price used to reflect average home prices in most areas, rather than the mean or mode? Should all people have similar houses or is it fair that some houses are much more expensive than others? Why or why not?
2. Some universities use SAT and ACT scores to determine whether to accept students. How can those two different scores be compared when they are on different scales and have completely different numeric values? Do you think test scores are a fair way to determine entrance eligibility to a college or university? Why or why not?
3. If the median income for a certain area is far above poverty level, does that mean the area has no problem with poverty? Why or why not? What would have to be true about the dispersion in order to be sure that there is no

poverty problem in this area? Are there any other statistics that are important to understand in order to answer this question?

Chapter 4: Probability Distributions

In this chapter we will discuss random variables, probability distributions and binomial probabilities.

Random Variables

A <u>random variable</u> x is a rule that assigns a single number to each outcome in the sample space. It can also be thought of as a single value that is determined by chance.

<u>Example:</u> Suppose we randomly select a family with three children from the population and count the number of boys in the family. The random variable x assigns the number of boys to each outcome.

Outcome	Random Variable x
BBB	3
BBG	2
BGB	2
BGG	1
GBB	2
GBG	1
GGB	1
GGG	0

Continuous vs. Discrete Random Variable

Definitions of continuous and discrete data were discussed in chapter 1 of this text.

A discrete random variable can assume only a countable set of values. Examples of discrete random variable are: shoe size, the dollar amount spent at the grocery store (Note that dollar amount is fixed to only two decimal places), the number of tails if three coins are tossed, sum of the numbers if a pair of dice are rolled, etc. A continuous random variable can assume the value of any continuous real number in a certain range. Examples are heights, weights, etc.

Probability Distributions

The possible values of the random variable in the previous example are 0, 1, 2, and 3 boys. Suppose we associate to each value of x its probability. The result is a probability distribution.

$P(x=0) = 1/8$
$P(x=1) = 3/8$
$P(x=2) = 3/8$
$P(x=3) = 1/8$

We can then organize the random variables and their associated probability in a Probability Distribution table. You should note that this is set up the same way as a Frequency Distribution Table except that the probability is now associated with each outcome rather than the frequency.

Random Variable: x	P(x)
0	1/8
1	3/8
2	3/8
3	1/8

Requirements for a Probability Distribution

In a probability distribution, the distribution must contain all possible distinct outcomes. Therefore, the sum of the probabilities must add up to one. Also, the probability values must be valid so they must be between zero and one. In summary, the following conditions must be satisfied.

1. Sum $[P(x)] = 1$
2. $0 \leq P(x) \leq 1$ for each $P(x)$

If either of these conditions is not met, then the table is not a valid probability distribution.

Histogram for a Probability Distribution

A probability distribution is very similar to a relative frequency table. You construct it the same way as a relative frequency distribution, with the percentage or probability as the vertical scale. Here is a histogram for the example above:

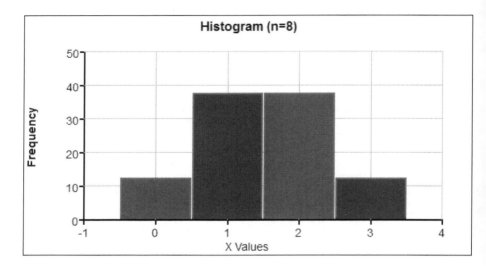

Mean and Standard Deviation of a Probability Distribution

The mean or expected value of a probability distribution is found in the same way as the mean of a relative frequency distribution table. Since the sum of the probabilities in the second column is 1, it can be shown that the mean of a probability distribution is $\Sigma(x*P(x))$. It means you take the product of the first column value of x times the second column value of probability; then add the results up for each row. For the last example we will have:

mean (or expected value) = $(0)(1/8)+(1)(3/8)+(2)(3/8)+(3)(1/8) = 12/8 = 1.5$.

The result indicates that each time we select a family with three children, the expected number of boys will be 1.5 out of 3. The expected value could be a decimal number and it does not have to be a value from the original data set. In the above example, if we select a family with three children over and over a large number of times and record the number of boys, then calculate the mean of the number of boys recorded from the observations, the mean will be close to 1.5. Theoretically, according to the "Law of Large Numbers," if we repeat the experiment an infinite number of times, the mean of the number of boys will be exactly 1.5.

Note: You can find the mean and the standard deviation of a probability distribution the exact same way that you computed the mean and standard deviation of a frequency distribution table.

Binomial Probability Distributions

A distribution is referred to as a binomial probability distribution provided that all the following conditions are met.

1- There is a fixed number of n trials.
2- The trials are independent of one another.

3- The outcomes of each trial are classified into two categories. The categories are referred to as "success" and "failure."
4- The probability of success remains constant in all trials.

There is slight flexibility on the requirement for independent if the number of trials is less than 5% of the original sample size.

Notations

n = the number of trials
P(S) = p = probability of success in one trial
P (F) = q = 1-p = probability of failure in one trial
x = the number of successes in n trials with
$0 \leq x \leq n$
P(x) = the probability of getting exactly x successes in n trials.

Computing Binomial Probability P(x) of Exactly x Successes in n Trials

Method 1 – Most statisticians use software for these calculations. You should strongly consider using Excel, Statdisk, Minitab, SPSS, or a calculator such as the TI-83 plus.

For Statdisk you would select "Analysis" – "Probability Distributions" – "Binomial Distribution" and then enter the values for n and P that are given in the problem. The results for P(x) are then listed in a table form along with the mean and standard deviation.

Example: For a binomial experiment find the probability of exactly 4 successes in 6 trials given that p=0.8. Use the binomial formula.

Solution: n = 6, p = 0.8, q = 0.2, x = 4

Binomial Probability			— ▢ ✕
Num Trials, n:	6		Evaluate
Success Prob, p:	0.8		

Mean:	4.8000		
St Dev:	0.9798		
Variance:	0.9600		

x	P(x)	P(x or fewer)	P(x or greater)
0	0.0000640	0.0000640	1.0000000
1	0.0015360	0.0016000	0.9999360
2	0.0153600	0.0169600	0.9984000
3	0.0819200	0.0988800	0.9830400
4	0.2457600	0.3446400	0.9011200
5	0.3932160	0.7378560	0.6553600
6	0.2621440	1.0000000	0.2621440

Help ?	Clear	Copy

Scrolling down to x=4 we see that P(x) is 0.2458 In Excel you would choose "Formulas" – "More Functions" – "Statistical" – "Binom.dist"- then enter the x value for s, n for trials, p for probability, and false for cumulative if you want only that value of x or else true for cumulative if you want the result for x or fewer.

Example: For a binomial experiment find the probability of exactly 4 successes in 6 trials given that p=0.8. Use the binomial formula.

Solution: s = x = 4, trials = n = 6, probability = p = 0.8, cumulative = false

Answer is 0.2458

Method 2 – Using the Formula

$$P(x) = \binom{n}{x} p^x q^{n-x} = \frac{n!}{x!\,(n-x)!} p^x q^{n-x}$$

<u>Example:</u> For a binomial experiment find the probability of exactly 4 successes in 6 trials given that p=0.8. Use the binomial formula.

Solution: n = 6, p = 0.8, q = 0.2, x = 4

$$P(x=4) = \binom{6}{4} 0.8^4 \, 0.2^2 = \frac{6!}{4!(6-4)!}(0.4096)(0.04) = \frac{(6)(5)(4)(3)(2)(1)}{(4)(3)(2)(1).(2)(1)}(0.4096)(0.04) = 0.2458$$

<u>Method 3 – Binomial Probability Distribution Table</u> can also be used for situations that fall within the boundaries of the table. However, tables are rarely used with the availability of computers.

<u>Mean and Standard Deviation of Binomial Probability Distributions</u>

Mean: $\mu = np$
Standard deviation: $\sigma = \sqrt{npq}$

* note that in Statdisk, the mean and standard deviation are computed along with the probability value.

Explorations

1. Construct three questions that could be answered using the Binomial Distribution and explain why you know the Binomial distribution is appropriate to use in each case.
2. Is there ever a time when a probability distribution should not add up to 1 or when the probability values will be less than 0 or greater than 1? Explain your answer. What might you do if you are ever reading a study that reflects a distribution that does not fit this criteria?

Critical Thinking and Values for Effective Problem Solving:

1. Explain how an understanding of probability can enhance responsible stewardship, respect, and community.
2. Almost anyone in the United States can play the lottery and lottery games come in many kinds. You might be surprised at how many people dedicate $50 (or more) a week to playing lotto games. But can the game you choose significantly affect you chances of winning? For the next two exercises you

75

will need to use the internet to find information.

Choose a state which runs lotteries.

a. Calculate your odds of winning if you spend $1 on an entry.

b. Calculate your odds of winning if you spend $50 on an entry.

c. Compare these odds to the odds of being in a car accident, plane crash, struck by lightning, or hit by a meteorite. (These numbers are out there so search for them!)

While many states run lotteries, most prohibit individuals and businesses from doing so. Is that ethical?

Court cases have held bartenders liable for serving alcohol to someone who is already drunk. Gambling is an addiction like alcohol. Should a state be liable for selling lotto tickets to a gambling addict?

What view might people have of the Lottery if they combine an understanding of Statistics and Respect?

Social Justice in the News:

1. Find an example in the news where a probability (or likelihood or expectation) is expressed as less than zero or greater than 100 or a distribution does not add up to

100%. Explain the bias that is reflected in the article by using the inappropriate statistic.

2. Go to a newspaper database and search for "probability". Choose one of the articles from your search results and explain how the term Probability is used in that article. Also explain why the given probability is or is not used correctly in the article and whether it is used to sway the reader. Don't forget to cite your article. How or why do you think that some authors would use probability to support their point of view? Does the use of probability mean the author's perspective is the correct perspective? Why or why not?

3. Research the lottery in the news to find out what socio-economic group purchases the most lottery tickets? What economic impact has the lottery had for this group? Is it ethical that our government is running and promoting the lottery?

Chapter 5: Normal Probability Distributions

A normal probability distribution is a symmetric bell shaped distribution with a continuous random variable and an exponential function that defines the points on the graph of the distribution. When analyzing data in various fields of both life and physical sciences, we encounter many examples of distributions that are bell shaped and symmetric. Furthermore, there are many applied examples of distributions with continuous or discrete random variables that are nearly normal and can be analyzed using properties of normal distributions.

In this chapter we will discuss the properties of normal distributions and will demonstrate how to calculate probabilities associated with normal distributions and how to apply them to real life application problems.

Properties of Normal Distributions

As stared earlier, the set of all points on a normal distribution curve are defined by a mathematical function. Consequent concepts from mathematics are used to analyze normal distributions. It can be shown that when data has a normal distribution, approximately 68% of the data fall within 1 standard deviation of the mean, approximately

95% fall within 2 standard deviations of the mean, and approximately 99.7% of the data fall within 3 standard deviations of the mean. This is called the Empirical Rule and implies that almost all data can be found within 3 standard deviations of the mean. Since the z-score measures the number of standard deviations that a data point is away from the mean, almost all z-scores fall between -3 and 3, or within 3 standard deviations of the mean. Most z-scores fall between -2 and 2, or within 2 standard deviations of the mean. The data with z-score less than -2 or greater than 2 is referred to as unusual.

An extremely important result from calculus that we shall use to calculate probabilities of normal distributions is the fact that the probability that a random variable falls between points a and b and the area under the graph of a normal distribution from a to b are identical. Therefore, we have the following.

$P(a \leq x \leq b)$
= probability that the random variable x falls between a and b
= area under the graph of the normal distribution from a to b
= percentage or proportion of the population between a and b

The total area under the graph of a normal curve is the same as the probability of the entire population or 1 or 100%. Furthermore, since a normal distribution is perfectly symmetric, the area to the left of the mean equals the area to the right of the mean equals 0.5. Therefore we have the following result.

Total area under the graph of a normal curve = P(-∞≤x≤∞) = 1
Area under the curve to the left of the mean = P(-∞≤mean) = 0.5
Area under the curve to the right of the mean = P(mean≤∞) = 0.5

Standard Normal Distributions

Definition

By definition, a standard normal distribution is a normal distribution with mean = 0 and standard deviation =1. It is easy to verify that in a standard normal distribution, for each value x of data, x = z-score. We can directly use the standard normal distribution table or use a statistical software or calculator such as Excel, Statdisk, or TI 83/84, to compute the probabilities for a standard normal distribution.

Obviously the normal distribution curve properties that we discussed earlier apply to the standard normal distribution.

1. Total area under the graph of a normal curve = $P(-\infty \le z \le \infty) = 1$
2. Area under the curve to the left of the mean = $P(-\infty \le 0) = 0.5$
3. Area under the curve to the right of the mean = $P(0 \le \infty) = 0.5$
4. $P(a \le z \le b)$
   = probability that the z falls between a and b
   = area under the graph of the standard normal distribution from a to b.
   = percentage or proportion of the z scores between a and b

Every normal distribution is comparable to the standard normal distribution. You can "convert" any normal distribution to the standard normal distribution by replacing the x values with the z-scores. In the future, we often convert normal distributions to standard normal distributions before calculating the probabilities.

Example 1: Find $P(z < -1.68)$.

Solution: The standard normal distribution table provides area to the left of each given z score. According to the table, $P(z < -1.68) = 0.0465$. We can use Statdisk and select Analysis – Probability distributions – Normal distribution.

Then enter -1.68 for the z-score and look at the output designated for the left since we want z less than -1.68.

Example 2: Find P(z > -1.68) .

Solution: The standard normal distribution table gives us area to the left of z = -1.68. Area to the right of z = -1.68 will be the total area or 1 minus this area. Therefore we have:

P(z > -1.68) =1 - P(z < -1.68) = 1- 0.0465 = 0.9535. Here we did not need to use the software because we know that the area to the left and right of -1.68 must add up to 1. However, you may also look at the previous Statdisk screen to see that the area to the right is also given directly as 0.9535

Example 3: Find P(-1.68 <z < 1.20)

Solution: In this example, we want the area between the two z-scores. Once we find area to the left of each score, we can subtract the smaller region from the larger region and that will gave us the area between the two scores:

P(-1.68 <z < 1.20) = P(z < 1.20) – P(z < -1.68) = 0.0.8849 – 0.0465 = 0.8384

Example 4: Find the 80 percentile z-score, that is the z-score that separates the bottom 80% of all the z-scores from the top 20% of the data.

Solution: If we want to use the standard normal distribution table, then we need to look for the area to the left closest to 0.8. The closest area to this value in the table is 0.7995, which corresponds to z = 0.84.

To use Stadisk, we can enter the cumulative area to the left. Since we want to separate the top 20% that means 0.80 is the cumulative area to the left and see that the z-score is 0.84.

Note that probabilities are rounded to 4 decimal places to match the tables that were used to find the values before Statistical software became popular. Z-scores are rounded to 2 decimal places.

Applications of Normal Distributions

As stated earlier, we can "convert" any normal curve to the standard normal curve by replacing the x values with the z-scores. We can then apply the methods discussed earlier to calculate the probabilities of any given normal distribution. The same is true if we want to find the data value that separates particular probabilities, such as the top 30%. Statdisk, TI 83/84 or other statistical software or calculators may be used to directly calculate the probabilities.

Example: The IQ scores for a population have a mean of 100 and standard deviation of 15. What percentage of the population has IQ score between 95 and 110?

Solution: We want to find P(95 ≤ x ≤ 110) for a normal distribution with mean = 100 and sd = 15. For this problem, we first need to convert all the x values to z scores.

$$Z = \frac{x-100}{15} = \frac{95-100}{15} = -5/15 = -0.33$$

$$Z = \frac{x-100}{15} = \frac{110-100}{15} = 10/15 = 0.67$$

P(90 ≤ x ≤ 110) = P(- 0.33 ≤ z ≤ 0.67)

Once you have the z-values of -0.33 and 0.67, you can use your software or calculator to find the probability to the left of each in order to take the difference between the two probability values

P(- 0.33 ≤ z ≤ 0.67) = 0.7486 – 0.3707 = 0.3779.

That means the percentage of the population with IQ scores between 95 and 110 is roughly 37.79%.

Example: For the example above, find the IQ score that separates the top 70% of all the IQ scores from the rest.

Solution: Whether you use the normal distribution table or Statdisk, you first need to find the cumulative area to the left, which is 1-0.70 or 0.30. The area closest to 0.30 in the table is 0.3015, which corresponds to z = -0.52. Now use the formula to solve for x.

$$-0.52 = \frac{x - 100}{15} \quad \text{or} \quad x = (-0.52)(15) + 100 = 92.2$$

Sampling Distribution of the Sample Means

The distribution of the means of all possible samples of size n taken from a population with a mean μ and standard deviation σ is called the sampling distribution of the sample means obtained from all samples of size n. The mean and the standard deviation of this new distribution are respectively referred to by $\mu_{\bar{x}}$ and $\sigma_{\bar{x}}$. It can be shown that

(1) $\mu_{\bar{x}} = \mu$

(2) $\sigma_{\bar{x}} = \sigma / \sqrt{n}$. $\sigma_{\bar{x}}$ is called the standard error of the mean,

It can also been shown that if the original sampled population has a normal distribution, then the sampling distribution of the means obtained from all samples of a given size n will be normal.

Many important theorems of inferential statistics are valid under the assumption that the sampling distribution of the means is normal. If the original population is normal, then the sampling distribution of the means is normal, but what if the original population is not normal?

The Central Limit Theorem

For sample size n>30, the sampling distribution of the sample means can be approximated by a normal distribution With mean $\mu_{\bar{x}} = \mu$ and standard deviation $\sigma_{\bar{x}} = \sigma / \sqrt{n}$.

Clearly the sampling distribution of the means is much narrower than the original distribution. As the sample size n increases, the standard deviation $\sigma_{\bar{x}}$ of the sampling distribution of the means becomes smaller.

Example:
A sampled population with mean of 500 and standard deviation of 25 is far from normal. What does the Central Limit Theorem say about the

sampling distribution of the means obtained from samples of size a) n=25, and b) n=100?

Solution:
  a) Since n=25 is not greater than 30, the Central Limit Theorem does not apply. We cannot conclude that the sampling distribution of the means obtained from all samples of size n=25 is normal.
  b) Since n=100 is greater than 30, the Central Limit Theorem does apply. We can conclude that the sampling distribution of the means obtained from all samples of size n=100 can be approximated by a normal distribution with mean $\mu_{\bar{x}} = \mu = 500$ and standard   deviation

  $$\sigma_{\bar{x}} = \sigma / \sqrt{n} = 25 / \sqrt{100} = 2.5$$

Explorations

Team Exercises in the News:

1. Find an example that uses the Normal Distribution in the news. Using a set of data like the one you found described, do the calculations for the Normal Distribution to see if you arrive at the same result. What can you conclude about the article you found? Be sure to include all of your work and the citation for your article.

2. Find at least 3 examples of continuous and 3 examples of discrete data in the news. Label each and include the citation for the article where the data was found.

Critical Thinking and Values for Effective Problem Solving:

1. If the sample is bias, how can you work with the Normal Distribution to get valid results? Explain your answer. What should you do to prevent a situation like that? Why might Respect be important in this situation?
2. How are the values of Integrity and Respect important when determining whether to apply the Normal Distribution and use the results?
3. How might the Normal Distribution be used to enhance responsible stewardship and Respect?

Writing across the Curriculum:

1. What are the criteria that must be met in order to use the Normal Distribution? Why can the distribution not be used if those criteria are not met?
2. Why is there more than one process for the Normal Distribution? Why are extra steps needed if the mean is not zero and the standard deviation is not one?

Social Justice across the Curriculum:

1. Scores and relative standing allow a researcher to compare results from two different groups in order to see which outcome has a better relative standing such as comparing ACT and SAT scores for college entrance or comparing Big East and Big 10 basketball standings. Would the same comparison be valid if the conferences being compared were the Big 10 and the NJCAA? Why or why not? What are some examples when relative standing is not valid? What are some things to consider when comparing outcomes from two different groups to determine whether the relative standing between the groups is relevant or not? What can this question have to do with Social Justice?

2. At SAT.org you can find the average scores by state as well as different ethnic backgrounds. When comparing states, why is the average not necessarily reflective of the average student level between some states? For example, what is a major difference between the group of students from Massachusetts who take the test and the students from Kentucky that set the expectation scores will be higher in Massachusetts?

Chapter 6: Estimates & Sample Sizes

Perhaps the most practical application of statistics is to make inferences about a parameter of a population by analyzing the statistics of an unbiased randomly selected sample from the population. In practice, we always have access to all the data from the sample. Once we calculate the statistic of the sample, we can use theories of statistics to:

> 1- Compute an interval of values that can be used to estimate the parameter of the population.
> 2- Decide whether a statement about the value or range of values of the parameter of the population is correct.

The first problem which is known as the "confidence interval" is discussed in this chapter. In the next chapter, we will study the second problem known as "hypothesis testing."

Definitions

A <u>point estimate</u> is a single value used to approximate a population parameter. Some statistics are better estimates of the population parameter than others. The mean of a sample is a good point estimate of the population mean. A sample proportion is a good point estimate for a population proportion. However, a sample mode would not usually be a good point estimate for a population mode.

Example: In order to predict the results of a future election for the mayor of a particular town, a random survey of 500 people was conducted. 150 of those participating in the survey expressed that they would vote for candidate A. The proportion $\hat{p}$ = 150/500 or 0.30 of the sample is used as a point estimate for the true proportion p of the population of the entire town voting for candidate A.

Example: A student at a particular university wishes to estimate the mean GPA of all students enrolled at the university. Since she has no access to the data for the entire population of students, she decides to survey students attending her statistics class. She uses the mean GPA $\bar{x}$ = 2.78 of her classmates as the point estimate mean GPA μ of the entire population of all students at the university. Obviously this is not a good point estimate because the sample is not a random sample.

A confidence interval is an interval used to estimate the true value of a population parameter. Although a point estimate is the best single value guess, it is unlikely that the population parameter is exactly that value. As a result, we prefer to use a confidence interval which gives a range of values that the population parameter likely falls within. The center of the confidence interval is the point estimate for the population parameter, while the width of this interval is determined by the margin of error E. For example, suppose that the proportion $\hat{p}$ of the sample that is used to estimate the population proportion p is 0.30. Further, suppose that based on the assumptions of the problem, the margin of error is determined to be 0.02. That means we add and subtract 0.02 from the sample proportion of 0.30 to get the confidence interval of (0.28, 0.32) for the population proportion, p. We then conclude that the population proportion is expected to be between 0.28 and 0.32.

The <u>confidence level</u> or the <u>degree of confidence</u> is the probability or the proportion of times that the true parameter of the population falls within the bounds of the confidence interval, provided that the confidence interval estimation process is repeated a large number of times. The confidence level is expressed as the probability $1-\alpha$.

The maximum likely difference between the observed sample statistic and the true value of the population parameter is called the <u>margin of error E</u>. In other words, E is the maximum distance we would expect the population parameter to be away from the sample statistic (point estimate). That means we subtract E from point estimate in order to find the minimum or left side value of the confidence interval and we add E to the point estimate in order to find the maximum, or right side value of the confidence interval.

A critical value is the z-score or the t value separating the values of the sample statistics that are likely to occur from those that are unlikely to occur. The critical values are denoted by $\pm z_{\alpha/2}$ (or $\pm t_{\alpha/2}$). So a critical value is the z or t score that separates the area $\alpha/2$ in each of the tails, or ends, of the distribution.

Estimating a population proportion

Assumptions

In order to use the techniques of this chapter to estimate a population proportion, the following assumptions must be true.

1- The sample is a simple random sample.
2- The conditions of a binomial distribution are satisfied.
3- $np \geq 5$ and $nq \geq 5$, which implies that we can use the normal distribution to approximate the binomial distribution.

Notations

p = proportion of the sampled population

$\hat{p}$ = x / n = sample proportion. x is the number of successes in a sample size of n. This is the point estimate for the true population proportion of successes

$\hat{q} = 1 - \hat{p}$ = proportion of failures in a sample of size n

Confidence Interval for the Population Proportion p

Proportion of the sample is used as the point estimate for the proportion of the population. Proportion of the sample is located at the center of the confidence interval. We can obtain the endpoints of the interval by adding and subtracting the margin of error E. The sample statistic can be calculated from the sample data, if it is not given explicitly in the problem. The margin of error is given by:

$$E = z_{\alpha/2}\sqrt{\frac{\hat{p}\hat{q}}{n}}$$

The confidence interval may be expressed by one of the following notations:

$$(\hat{p} - E, \hat{p} + E) \quad \text{or} \quad (\hat{p} \pm E) \quad \text{or} \quad (\hat{p} - E < p < \hat{p} + E)$$

These are three different forms of describing the same confidence interval. You may use any form unless one is specified.

Example: A simple random sample of 30 volleyball serves was taken from a team. According to the sample, 21 players made their serve and 9 players missed. Find a 95% confidence interval for the proportion of times the team players make their serve.

Solution: We see that $\hat{p} = 21/(21+9) = 21/30 = 0.7$ so $\hat{q} = 1 - \hat{p} = 1 - 0.7 = 0.3$

For E we will first find $z_{\alpha/2} = z_{.05/2} = z_{.025}$ or the z score that separates the top 2.5% from the bottom 97.5% (with a 95% confidence level that means you have 2.5% on the bottom and 2.5% on the top. For the positive z-score we only look at the top value). We can look this up in a table, use Excel, or in Statdisk select "Analysis" – "Probability Distributions" – "Normal Distribution" and enter the "cumulative area to the left" as 0.975 to get the z-value of 1.96. (see the diagram below)

Statdisk

File   Edit   Analysis   Data   Datasets   Window   Help

Sample

Probability Distributions	▶	Normal Distribution
Sample Size Determination	▶	Student-t Distribution
Confidence Intervals	▶	Chi-Square Distribution
Hypothesis Testing	▶	F Distribution
Correlation and Regression		Binomial Distribution
Multiple Regression		Poisson Distribution
Goodness-of-Fit	▶	
Contingency Tables		
One-Way Analysis of Variance		
Two-Way Analysis of Variance		
Sign Test	▶	
Wilcoxon Tests	▶	
Kruskal-Wallis Test		
Rank Correlation		
Runs Test		
Bootstrap Resampling		
Fisher Exact Test		
McNemar's Test		
Odds Ratio and Relative Risk		

Help   Print Data   Data Tools

Statdisk

File   Edit   Analysis   Data   Datasets   Window   Help

Sample Editor

Normal Distribution

Enter one value, then click
Evaluate to find the other value.

z Value:

Cumulative area   .975
from the left:

Evaluate

z Value: 1.959962
Prob Dens: 0.0584453

Cumulative Probs
Left: 0.975000
Right: 0.025000
2 Tailed: 0.050000
Central: 0.950000
As Table A-2: 0.975000

Print   Copy

That means we can find the margin of error E. Now we have $E = z_{\alpha/2}\sqrt{\dfrac{\hat{p}\hat{q}}{n}} = 1.96\sqrt{\dfrac{(0.7)(0.3)}{30}} = 0.164$.

Since $\hat{p}$ =0.7 and E=0.164, the confidence interval will be (0.7-0.164, 0.7+0.164) = (0.536, 0.864). Resulting in the expectation that we have 95% confidence that the true proportion of times the team will make their serve is between 53.6% and 86.4% of the time.

Sample Size Required to Estimate the Population Proportion p

Most of the problems you work are already set up in class. However, the purpose of these techniques is to be able to conduct studies yourself. When you are planning a study, you need to determine how large your sample should be, so that the margin of error would not exceed a certain percentage point. There are many factors to consider, such as time, money, and how much error you are willing to accept. If you start with the amount of error you are willing to accept, you can solve the margin of error formula for the sample size n. Time and money, or lack thereof, might impact the decision of how much error you are willing to accept. One important concept to keep in mind is to always round your sample size up. No matter how small the decimal portion, you must round a decimal number up to the next whole number in order to guarantee the given or required level of accuracy.

The appropriate sample size to estimate p can be obtained by solving $E = z_{\alpha/2}\sqrt{\dfrac{\hat{p}\hat{q}}{n}}$ for n to get:

$$n = \frac{(z_{\alpha/2})^2 \, \hat{p}\hat{q}}{E^2}$$, where n is rounded up to the next whole number unless n is a whole number.

If $\hat{p}$ is not known, then use $\hat{p} = \hat{q} = 0.5$. According to calculus, this will result in the largest possible product, making the largest possible value for n so you will guarantee you are keeping the margin of error below the required value for the study.

Suppose that in the previous example, we decided the margin of error of 0.164 or 16.4% was too large and we want to estimate the true proportion of times the team will serve the ball in the court with a margin of error under 5%. That means we do not want the margin of error exceed E=.05. From previous study, we already know $\hat{p} = 0.7$ and $\hat{q} = 0.3$. We also know that the critical value is z = 1.96. Using the given values, the sample size would be:

$$n = \frac{(z_{\alpha/2})^2 \, \hat{p}\hat{q}}{E^2} = \frac{(1.96)^2 (0.7)(0.3)}{0.05^2} = 322.7; \text{ rounded}$$
up to 323

Note that if $\hat{p}$ and $\hat{q}$ were not known, then we would use $\hat{p} = \hat{q} = 0.5$ to get:

$$n = \frac{(z_{\alpha/2})^2 \hat{p}\hat{q}}{E^2} = \frac{(1.96)^2(0.5)(0.5)}{0.05^2} = 384.16;$$

rounded up to 385

It is very important to round this number up because a number rounded down will not quite guarantee the level of accuracy needed. That means 323 serves will be needed in order to be able to construct a confidence interval that will provide an estimate of the true proportion of serves the team will make that is within 5% of the true proportion of serves the team makes.

Rounding

Always round the sample size up when your result is not a whole number. For example, n=55 would remain n=55 while n=55.1 would become n=56.

Round confidence interval values for proportion problems to at least to three significant digits.

You can also use statistical software for sample size. For example, you can solve this problem using Statdisk by selecting "Analysis"- "Sample

Size Determination" – "Estimate Proportion" and then enter the confidence level of 95% (1-0.05), margin of error of 0.05 and sample proportion of 0.7 to get n=323. This result is already rounded to the correct whole number.

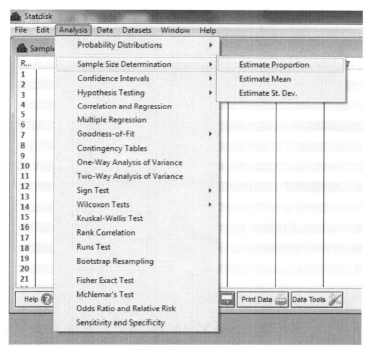

Estimating a Population Mean: σ known

When estimating a population mean, there are two different cases that we must consider.

Case 1: The standard deviation of the population, σ, is known.
Case 2: The standard deviation of the population, σ, is unknown.

The most common error in constructing confidence interval for a population mean is to confuse the two cases and use σ as the sample standard deviation rather than the population standard deviation.

Assumptions for Case 1 (σ is known):

1- The sample is a simple random sample.
2- The standard deviation of the population, σ, is known.
3- At least one of the following conditions is satisfied: the sampled population has a normal distribution or the sample size n > 30.

Confidence Interval for the Population Mean μ with σ Known

Similar to the proportion problem, the confidence interval for the mean of a population has the sample statistic as the center value, and to get the endpoints of the interval, the margin of error is subtracted from, and added to that value. The difference is that the sample statistic in the center is now the mean of the sample rather than the proportion of the sample, and the margin of error is calculated differently when we are working with the mean.

Margin of error: $E = z_{\alpha/2}\, \sigma / \sqrt{n}$

Confidence Interval: $(\bar{x} - E, \bar{x} + E)$ or $(\bar{x} \pm E)$ or $(\bar{x} - E < \mu < \bar{x} + E)$

Once again we have the same three forms that are different notations to represent the same interval.

Example: Suppose we want to estimate the mean IQ score of the adult population of a town. A simple random sample of 40 adults results in a mean of 101.2. The standard deviation σ of the population is known to be 14.8. Assume that a 98% confidence level is desired.

Solution:
We have a simple random sample of size n> 30. We also know that the mean of the sample is $\bar{x} = 101.2$ and the standard deviation of the population σ is 14.8. Since σ is known, we must use normal distribution to calculate the critical value. The area in each tail is (1-0.98)/2=0.01. The area to the left of the critical value is 0.01+0.98=0.99. The closest area in the normal distribution table is 0.9901, which gives $z_{\alpha/2} = 2.33$. Margin of error E can be calculated using the formula: $E = z_{\alpha/2}\, \sigma / \sqrt{n} =$ $(2.33)(14.8)/\sqrt{40} \approx 5.45$

The confidence interval is calculated by simplifying $\bar{x} \pm E$. Therefore we have:

101.2 ± 5.45   or   (95.75, 106.65)   or
$95 \cdot 75 < \mu < 106 \cdot 65$

We are 98% confident that the true mean IQ score for the population of the town is the interval or (95.75, 106.65).

You can also use statistical software for this problem. In Statdisk you can select "Analysis" – "Confidence Interval" – "Mean-onesample" and enter the confidence level of 0.98, sample size of 40, sample mean of 102.2 and population standard deviation of 14.8. Remember to enter the 14.8 as the population standard deviation rather than sample standard deviation.

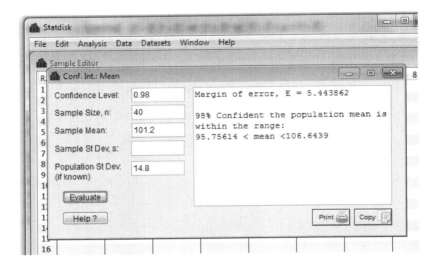

Sample Size Required to Estimate the Population Mean μ

The appropriate sample size to estimate the Population Mean μ is again obtained by solving the margin of error formula, $E = z_{\alpha/2}\, \sigma/\sqrt{n}$ for n:

$$n = \left(\frac{z_{\alpha/2}\, \sigma}{E}\right)^2$$

Remember to round up. You may also use statistical software choosing to estimate the mean rather than the proportion this time.

Example: Suppose you are trying out a new exercise routine designed to increase strength. How many people would you have to test to determine if their strength has improved given that the mean starting strength was to do 49.3 push-ups with a standard deviation of 3.4 push-ups, if you want your estimation of the true mean of the number of push-ups for the entire population to be within 1 push-up? Use a 95% confidence level.

Solution: You can use the formula above with $z_{\alpha/2} = 1.96$ for a 95% confidence level, σ is given as 3.4, and $E = 1$ or you can use Statdisk and choose "Analysis" – "Sample size determination" – "Estimate Mean" and enter 95% for confidence level, 1 for Margin of Error, and 3.4 for sample standard deviation to see that n=45 as the required sample size.

Sample Size: Mean	
Confidence level: 0.95	Required sample size is: 45
Margin of Error, E: 1	Assumed either infinite
Population St Dev: 3.4	population or the population was sampled with replacement
Population Size: (if known)	
Evaluate	
Help ?	Print Copy

Estimating a Population Mean: σ unknown

Here we will continue to estimate a population Mean. This time the population standard deviation

108

is not known and will therefore not be included in any of the calculations. You will notice that the general approach and the formulas are similar to the case with σ known, except that the standard deviation σ of the population is replaced by the standard deviation s of the sample and the z values are replaced by the t values. This is a good time to discuss the t-distribution.

Properties of t Distributions

A *t*-distribution is a family of distributions, where each curve has a shape similar to a normal curve. However, each t distribution curve is shorter than the normal curve and is thicker at the tail ends. As the sample size n becomes larger, the shape of the *t*-distribution curve becomes closer to the shape of the standard normal curve. For large n, we can use normal distribution to approximate t-distribution.

Each curve in the family of *t*-distributions is identified by a number called degree of freedom df. Degree of freedom is defined to be df = n-1. When reading the t values from the t-distribution table for a confidence interval problem, you will need df and the sum of areas in the two tails. In the future chapter, when working on the hypothesis problem, you will need df and the area in one tail or the sum of the areas in the two tails.

As n becomes larger, the *t*-distribution curve becomes closer to the standard normal curve.

Assumptions for Case 2 (σ is unknown):

We again have assumptions that must be met in order to use the techniques in this section. Notice that the second assumption is the only one that has changed.

1. The sample is a simple random sample.
2. The population standard deviation is not known.
3. At least one of the following conditions is satisfied: The sampled population has a normal distribution or the sample size n > 30.

Confidence Interval for the Population Mean μ with σ Unknown

If the population standard deviation σ of the population is unknown, then the Student t-distribution provides a better approximation for the probabilities than the usual normal distribution. In this case, in all the confidence interval formulas, σ is replaced by the sample standard deviation s, and the z values are replaced by the t values. The margin of error and the confidence interval formulas are modified as follows.

Margin of error: $E = t_{\alpha/2} \; s/\sqrt{n}$

Confidence Interval: $(\bar{x} - E, \bar{x} + E)$ or $(\bar{x} \pm E)$ or $(\bar{x} - E < \mu < \bar{x} + E)$

Where $t_{\alpha/2}$ has df = n-1 degrees of freedom.

You can use a Student t-distribution table for the values of t or you can determine them using statistical software. In Statdisk you can choose "Analysis" – "Probability Distributions" – "Student-t Distribution" and follow the prompts.

Notice that one prompt is now the cumulative area to the right rather than the left that is found in the normal distribution.

Example: Suppose we want to estimate the mean IQ score of the adult population of a town. A simple random sample of 40 adults results in a mean of 101.2 and a standard deviation of 14.8. Assume that a 98% confidence level is desired.

Solution:
This example is similar to the previous example with the big difference that the standard deviation of the population σ is unknown. We have a simple random sample of size n> 30. We also know that the mean of the sample is $\bar{x} = 101.2$ and the standard deviation of the sample s is 14.8. Since σ is unknown, we must use normal Student t-distribution to calculate the critical value. The area in two tails is 1-0.98=0.02 with df=n-1=39.

The Student t-distribution table gives $t_{\alpha/2} = 2.426$.
Margin of error E can be calculated using the formula:

$$E = t_{\alpha/2}\, s/\sqrt{n} = (2.426)(14.8)/\sqrt{40} \approx 5.68$$

The confidence interval is calculated by simplifying $\bar{x} \pm E$. Therefore we have:

101.2 ± 5.68   or   (95.52, 106.88)   or
$95 \cdot 52 < \mu < 106 \cdot 88$

We are 98% confident that the true mean IQ score for the population of the town is the interval or (95.52, 106.88).

Statdisk can be used to find the t-value for a 98% confidence interval by entering the degrees of freedom df = 39 and the cumulative area to the right would be half of $\alpha/2 = 0.02/2 = 0.01$. This gives a t value of 2.426.

The margin of error and the confidence interval can be calculated in Statdisk by selecting "Analysis" – "Confidence Intervals" – "Mean-One Sample" and enter the confidence level of 0.98, sample size of 40, sample mean of 102.2 and sample standard deviation of 14.8.

Notice that the result is slightly different when given a sample standard deviation rather than the population standard deviation, so you must be very careful you recognize which is given in the problem.

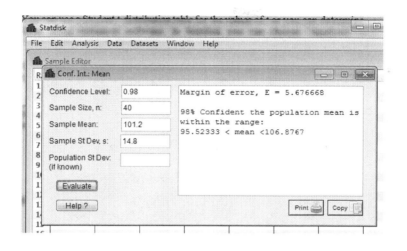

Determining Which Distribution to Use

Use the list of assumptions for each section to determine whether to use the Student t-distribution or the Normal distribution. For both either the sample size must be greater than 30 or the population must be normally distributed. If neither of these criteria is met, then you may not use either distribution.

If either the population is normally distributed or the sample size is greater than 30 (or both), then you determine whether to use z or t by whether the population standard deviation is known or unknown. We use z when we know the population standard deviation, σ. We use the Student t-distribution when the population standard deviation is unknown, meaning σ is not known.

Important Note: You should always keep in mind that in real life, the standard deviation σ of the population is hardly ever known. As a result the, you should heavily focus on the case where σ is unknown.

Explorations

Social Justice in the News:

1. Colleges and Universities have been required to provide equal access and opportunity. Recently the trend is moving toward equal outcomes. How are these two ideas different? Using the current news or data, construct or find a confidence interval to show proportion of access by a certain ethnic or socio economic group at a University of your choice. Then, construct a similar confidence interval for outcomes by that group, such as graduation rate compared to overall graduation rate. How do these two intervals compare?

2. In the past, part of the mission statement for the Statistical Association of America was "Using Our Discipline to Enhance Human Welfare". What do you think is meant by this, and why would it be important enough to include in a mission statement? Can you find any examples in the news that might be relevant to this mission?

Team exercises for Problem Solving and Critical Thinking:

1. Find a 95% confidence interval for your group's favorite team(s) to make it to the final play-off for that sport next year by using the proportion of the number of times they have made it to that playoff divided by the total number of seasons they have had. If your team has never made it to the final playoffs, then do another example for a team that is more worthy of you as a fan. How does this relate to the odds for betting on a team or game? Find current odds on a game and the confidence interval for one of the teams to win and see how the odds and confidence interval compare or do not compare. What other considerations might be taken into account when determining odds in favor of a specific outcome?

2. Find a confidence interval in the news or a news release and explain what the confidence interval means. Does the article appear to be constructing and using the confidence interval correctly? Is there anything else you can question or conclude from the given information? Can you find other articles that support the information from the confidence interval that you found?

Social Justice as a Team:

1. Find as many groups as you can that have been providing clean drinking water as part of their mission or objectives and that provide a cost analysis to provide one clean drinking water location. Summarize your findings in a table and find a confidence interval for the average cost of providing clean drinking water to one location.

Writing across the Curriculum:

1. There were three similar but different sets of assumptions in this section. Why are the assumptions necessary for each test?
2. Explain what a confidence interval is and how it helps you to better understand the parameter of the population you are interested in.

Values Across the Curriculum:

1. Why is determining an appropriate sample size important for responsible stewardship and Respect?
2. To ensure the integrity of statistical results, is a point estimate or a confidence interval a better estimate to use to report conclusions about a population parameter? Why?

Chapter 7: Hypothesis Testing

A hypothesis is a claim or a statement about a parameter of the population.   A statistical hypothesis test is a process by which we test the claim about a parameter of a population.   In this chapter we will only consider claims about mean or proportion of populations.

Similar to the confidence interval problem, we will develop techniques to test claims for three separate cases: population proportions, population mean with σ known, and population mean with σ unknown.

The main components of hypothesis testing common to all three cases mentioned above which we shall discuss in this chapter are:

- Given a claim, identify the statements of null hypothesis H_o and the alternative hypothesis H_1 in mathematical notation.
- Given a significance level α, find the critical z or t values.
- Given a significance level α, find the P-values.
- Given a claim and sample data, calculate the value of the test statistic.
- State the initial conclusion of the hypothesis test addressing the null hypothesis H_o.

- State the final conclusion of the hypothesis test addressing the original claim.

In addition, we will briefly discuss type I and type II errors.

H_0 and H_1

The null hypothesis H_0 is the statement that is initially tested by the hypothesis testing procedure. H_0 always assumes the form of equality. For proportion problems, H_0 looks like "p = a numerical value" and for mean problems it look like "μ = a numerical value." The statement of the alternative hypothesis does not contain any kind of equality. Here are three simple steps you need to follow to construct the statements of H_0 and H_1.

Step 1: Express the two opposing statements in mathematical language.
Step 2: H_1 is the statement that does not contain any kind of equality (i.e., $<, >, \neq$).
Step 3: The other statement contains some kind of equality. Change it to "=" and call it H_0.

Rejection of H_0 implies that you reject the statement that contains equality and you support the alternative hypothesis H_1.

Example 1: Claim: The average age of girls in Junior Girl Scouts is 10 years old.
Opposing statements:
$\mu = 10$ (claim)
$\mu \neq 10$

H_1: $\mu \neq 10$
H_0: $\mu = 10$

Example 2: Claim: The new RV models get at least 16 miles to the gallon.
Opposing statements:
$\mu \geq 16$ (claim)
$\mu < 16$

H_1: $\mu < 16$
H_0: $\mu = 16$

Example 3: Claim: It takes more than 20 minutes to read this section.
Opposing statements:
$\mu > 20$ (claim)
$\mu \leq 20$

H_1: $\mu > 20$
H_0: $\mu = 20$

The statement of the claim has absolutely nothing to do with identifying H_0 and H_1. You use the claim to come up with the two opposing statements. The only other place that you use the

120

claim is in the final conclusion when you need to address the claim and state whether you reject or support the claim.

Test Statistic

The test statistic is a numerical value derived from the sample. The test statistics is simply the z or t value of the statistic of the sample. The values for test statistic are calculated using the same formulas as earlier in this book.

Test statistic for proportion: $z = \dfrac{\hat{p} - p}{\sqrt{\dfrac{pq}{n}}}$

Test statistic for mean: $z = \dfrac{\bar{x} - \mu}{\dfrac{\sigma}{\sqrt{n}}}$ (σ known)   or

$t = \dfrac{\bar{x} - \mu}{\dfrac{s}{\sqrt{n}}}$ (σ unknown)

Later, we will use the test statistic to compare to the critical value to determine whether we reject or fail to reject H_0.

The Critical Region and the Critical Values

The critical region consists of all values of the test statistic which imply the rejection of H_0. A critical value is a z or t value that separates the critical region of the normal curve or student t-distribution curve from the rest.

Just like before, we can use software to calculate the values of the test statistics. If using Statdisk, we can choose "Analysis" – "Probability Distributions" and insert the appropriate area to the left or right of the test statistics.

The Significance Level α

The significance level, α is the probability that the test statistic will fall in the critical region when the null hypothesis is actually true. Therefore, α is the total area of the critical region. This is equal to the probability of a type I error.

Two Tailed and One Tailed Tests

Two Tailed Test: If H_1 contains "≠," H_0 is rejected if the test statistic falls too far to the left or too far to the right. The test is called a two tailed test and the critical region consists of a tail to the left and a tail to the right. The significance level α is the sum of the areas in the two tails and area in each tail is α /2.

Left Tailed Test: If H_1 contains "<," H_0 is rejected if the test statistic falls too far to the left. The test is called a left tailed test and the critical region

122

consists of only a tail to the left. The significance level α is the area in the left tail.

Right Tailed Test: If H_1 contains ">," H_0 is rejected if the test statistic falls too far to the right. The test is called a right tailed test and the critical region consists of only a tail to the right. The significance level α is the area in the right tail.

To determine whether the test is two tailed, left tailed, or right tailed, always look at the direction of H_1 (The statement that does not contain any kind of equality).

The Conclusion

The hypothesis procedure always results in a decision about H_0. The initial conclusion is always in the form "reject H_0" or "fail to reject H_0." We do not say "we support H_0" or "we do not support H_0." The justification is that H_0 is assumed to be true unless we have strong evidence to reject it in favor of H_1. The final conclusion must address the original claim. If the original claim is H_1, then the final conclusion will be in the form "support H_1" or "do not support H_1." Below we have provided examples of each possible scenario that you may encounter. For each example, you are given a claim and the initial conclusion, and asked to state the final conclusion in terms of the original claim.

Example 1: (The original claim is the statement of equality and initial conclusion is to reject H_0)
Original Claim: The average age of girls in Junior Girl Scouts is 10 years old.
Hypothesis test result (initial conclusion): reject H_0.

Solution:
Conclusion: Reject H_0. There is sufficient evidence to reject the claim that the average age of girls in Junior Girl Scouts is 10 years old.

Example 2: (The original claim is the statement of equality and initial conclusion is fail to reject H_0)
Original Claim: The average age of girls in Junior Girl Scouts is 10 years old.
Hypothesis test result (initial conclusion): fail to reject H_0

Solution:
Conclusion: Do not reject H_0. There is not sufficient evidence to reject the claim that the average age of girls in Junior Girl Scouts is 10 years old.

Example 3: (The original claim is H_1 and initial conclusion is to reject H_0)
Original Claim: It takes more than 20 minutes to read this section.
Hypothesis test result (initial conclusion): reject H_0

Solution:
Conclusion: Reject H_0. There is sufficient evidence to Support the claim that it takes more than 20 minutes to read this section.

Example 4: (The original claim is H_1 and initial conclusion is fail to reject H_0)
Original Claim: It takes more than 20 minutes to read this section.
Hypothesis test result (initial conclusion): fail to reject H_0

Solution:
Conclusion: Do not Reject H_0. There is not sufficient evidence to support the claim that it takes more than 20 minutes to read this section.

The original claim could be H_0 or H_1 depending on the statement of the problem.

The initial conclusion will always be in terms of H_0. It will be either "reject H_0" or "fail to reject H_0."

The final conclusion has to be worded in terms of the original claim. This is the only time in the procedure that you use the original claim.

Type I and Type II Errors

Obviously we want to make the right decision about the null hypothesis, H_0. There are two ways that we can go wrong, that is why they are called errors. First, we might conclude that H_0 is wrong and reject it, while in reality H_0 is true. This is called Type I error. Second, we might fail to reject H_0 when it is actually false. This is called type II error. Of course, we do not know an error was made because we may not know the true nature of H_0 or else we would not need the hypothesis test. You have to keep in mind that statistics is all about probabilities. No matter how careful we select our sample and conduct our analysis, there is always a probability or possibility that the result may not be valid. If the consequences of a wrong conclusion are catastrophic, then we must minimize the probability of type I or II errors. Typically H_0 is a statement that has been in place for a long time and we must avoid rejecting a true H_0 (type I error) as much as possible. Below is a table that might help you visualize these errors.

Decision	H_0 is true	H_0 is not true
Fail to reject H_0	Right (correct decision)	Type II error
Reject H_0	Type I error	Right (correct decision)

Hypothesis Testing Procedure

There are two different methods for Hypothesis testing: the critical value method and the P-value method. Both methods can be found in some statistical software packages such as Statdisk.

Critical Value Method:

1. State H_0 and H_1.

• Read the statement of the problem carefully.
• Express the original claim (The claim that shows up in the statement of the problem) in mathematical language.
• Write the opposite statement in mathematical language. The statement that does not contain "=" is H_1. Change the other statement to "=" and call it H_0.
• The original claim could be H_0 or H_1 depending on the statement of the problem.

2. Determine the critical values and the critical regions (This can be done using technology such as Statdisk).

• Always look at the direction of H_1 to determine whether the test is left tailed (negative Critical Value), right tailed (positive Critical Value), or two tailed (+/- for two Critical Values).

3. Calculate the value of the test statistic.

Proportion: $z = \dfrac{\hat{p} - p}{\sqrt{\dfrac{pq}{n}}}$

mean with σ known: $z = \dfrac{\bar{x} - \mu}{\dfrac{\sigma}{\sqrt{n}}}$ mean with

σ unknown: $t = \dfrac{\bar{x} - \mu}{\dfrac{s}{\sqrt{n}}}$

4. Determine whether the test statistic falls in the critical region

5. Make a decision about H_0

• The initial conclusion will always be in terms of H_0.
• Reject H_0 if the test statistic falls in the critical region.
• Fail to reject H_0 if the test statistic does not fall in the critical region.

6. Write a conclusion about the original claim.

• The final conclusion should be expressed in terms of the original claim.

P-Value Method:

The P-value method is very similar to the critical value method, except that in the 4th step we compare the area outside the critical region to the area outside the test statistic. The area outside the critical region is α while the area outside the test statistic is used to find P. For left or right tailed tests, the P-value is the area outside the test statistic. For two-tailed tests, the P-value is twice the area outside the test statistic. If the area outside the test statistic is smaller than the area outside the critical value, this implies that the test statistic is outside the critical region so we reject the null hypothesis. In other words, if $P<\alpha$ we reject H_0. Since α is known or determined for each problem, then by calculating the P-value you can compare the two numbers to make your initial conclusion and then finish the final conclusion the same as above. If the area outside the test statistic is larger than the critical region, we fail to reject the null hypothesis. That means, if $P > \alpha$ we fail to reject H_0.

The P-value method is used most often for people who use statistical software because the software calculates the P-value so it makes for a very simple comparison.

It is time to put this together with a few specific situations. For each Statistical test that is available for us to use, there is a list of criteria that must be met in order for the test results to be valid. You will see this list of requirements for each case below as "Assumptions". If these assumptions are not met, then we may not use the test of hypothesis.

Testing a Claim about a Population Proportion p
Assumptions

1. The sample observations are random.
2. The conditions of binomial distribution are satisfied.
3. $np \geq 5$ and $nq \geq 5$

➤ State H_0 and H_1.
➤ Determine the critical regions.
➤ Calculate the value of the test statistic:
$$z = \frac{\hat{p} - p}{\sqrt{\dfrac{pq}{n}}}.$$

➤ Determine whether the test statistic falls in the critical region or whether the P-value is greater or less than α.
➤ Make a decision about H_0 (Reject H_0 if the test statistic falls in the critical region).
➤ Write a final conclusion about the original claim.

Example: Use a 0.01 significance level to test the claim that the proportion of students who pass statistics in any given semester with a grade of D or better is at least 75%. In a simple random sample, there were 51 students and 31 passed the class with a grade of D or better.

Solution: Before we study the claim, we will check that the assumptions are met. It is a simple random sample, the conditions of the binomial distribution are met, and there are at least 5 success and 5 failures. Furthermore, we have:

$$n = 51 \text{ and the proportion of sample } \hat{p} = \frac{31}{51} \approx 0.6078$$

We will analyze the claim by going through all the steps of the hypothesis testing and then we will show how to use technology to solve the problem.

The first step is to write the claim in mathematical symbols. Since "at least" means greater than or equal to, we have $p \geq 0.75$. Therefore, the opposing statements are:
$p \geq 0.75$ (claim)
$p < 0.75$

We know that H_0 will contain the equality, so we can label these two statements as:
H_1: $p < 0.75$
H_0: $p = 0.75$

Next we need to find the critical values. Since H_1 is of the form "$<$," this is a left tailed test with area 0.01 in the tail. According to the normal distribution table, the z score associated with this area is z = -2.33. This is our only critical value. The region to the left of z = -2.33 is the critical region. We reject the null hypothesis if the test statistic falls in this region.

The test statistics is given by:

$$z = \frac{\hat{p} - p}{\sqrt{\dfrac{pq}{n}}} = \frac{0.6078 - 0.75}{\sqrt{\dfrac{(0.75)(0.25)}{51}}} \approx -2.34$$

It is a close call, but the critical value does fall in the critical region, and therefore, we reject the null hypothesis H_0 in the favor of the alternative hypothesis H_1.

The final conclusion has to address the claim ($p \geq 0.75$). Note that the initial conclusion is to reject H_0 and therefore reject the statement of equality. We conclude that at the significance level 0.01, there is sufficient evidence to reject the claim that the proportion of students who pass statistics in any given semester with a grade of D or better is at least 75%.

We can use Statdisk to select "Analysis" – "Hypothesis Testing" – "Proportion One Sample" and select "Pop Prop. > or = to Claimed Prop" along with a significance level of 0.01 and a claimed proportion of 0.75 (always the proportion in the claim and hypothesis). With a sample of 51 and with 31 successes we get the following results:

The test statistic is -2.3445 with a critical value of -2.3264 so we reject the null hypothesis since the test statistic is outside of the critical region. Or, we have a significance level of 0.01 with a P-value of 0.0095 so the p-value is smaller than the significance level so we reject the null hypothesis. Our initial conclusion is to "reject the null hypothesis" so our final conclusion is that the sample provides enough evidence to reject the claim that at least 75 percent of students pass Statistics each semester.

Testing a Claim about a Population Mean: σ known

Assumptions

1. The sample is a simple random sample.
2. σ is known (remember that σ is the population standard deviation)
3. At least one of the following conditions is satisfied: the population is normal or $n > 30$.

➤ State H_0 and H_1.
➤ Determine the critical values and the critical regions. The critical values will be z values.
➤ Calculate the value of the test statistic: $z = \dfrac{\bar{x} - \mu}{\dfrac{\sigma}{\sqrt{n}}}$.
➤ Determine whether the test statistic falls in the critical region.
➤ Make a decision about H_0 (reject H_0 if the test statistic falls in the critical region).
➤ Write a final conclusion about the original claim.

Example: At level of significance $\alpha = 0.05$, we want to test the claim that the mean time for students to read this section of the text is more than 20 minutes. A recent random sample of 45 people showed that it took on average 20.2 minutes to read this section. The population has a standard deviation of 1.3 minutes.

Solution:
In this example, we have a simple random sample with n>30 and standard deviation σ of the population known. Furthermore, we have sample size n=45, mean of the sample $\bar{x} = 20.2$, and standard deviation of the population σ=1.3.

As we did earlier, we will analyze the claim by going through all the steps of the hypothesis testing and then we will show how to use technology to solve the problem.

The two opposing statements are:
μ > 20 (claim)
μ ≤ 20

The statement that does not contain any kind of equality is called H_1. We change the other statement to "=" and call it H_o:
H_1: μ > 20
H_o: μ =20

Based on the direction of H_1, this is an example of a right-tailed test. The area in the tail is 0.05. Since standard deviation σ of the population is known, we use normal distribution to find the critical value. The area to the left of the critical value is 1-0.05=0.95. The critical value from the normal distribution table is 1.645.

The test statistics is calculated using the formula:

$$z = \frac{\bar{x} - \mu}{\frac{\sigma}{\sqrt{n}}} = \frac{20.2 - 20}{\frac{1.3}{\sqrt{45}}} \approx 1.03$$

Clearly the test statistic does not fall in the critical region. Therefore, the initial conclusion is that we do not reject the null hypothesis and the statement of equality stands. To finish the problem, we need to state our final conclusion in terms of the original claim ($\mu > 20$). The final conclusion is that at the significance level 0.05, we do not have sufficient evidence to support the claim that the mean time for students to read this section of the text is more than 20 minutes.

Here is how we use Statdisk to analyze this problem. We will select "Pop Mean > Claimed Mean" and then enter the sample size of 45 with the claimed mean of 20, sample mean of 20.2, and a standard deviation of 1.3 minutes.

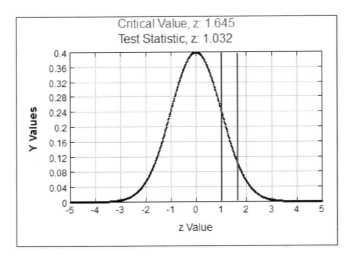

Hypothesis Testing: One Mean

5) Pop. Mean > Claimed Mean

Significance:	0.05
Claimed Mean:	20
Population St Dev: (if known)	1.3
Sample Size, n:	45
Sample Mean:	20.2
Sample St Dev, s:	

Evaluate

Plot

Help ?

```
Claim:     μ >  μ(hyp)

z Test
Test Statistic, z: 1.0320
Critical z:        1.6449
P-Value:           0.1510

90% Confidence interval:
19.88124 <  μ < 20.51876

Fail to Reject the Null
Hypothesis
Sample does not provide enough
evidence to support the claim
```

Print   Copy

In this example we fail to reject the null hypothesis because the test statistic does not fall out in the right tail past the critical value.

Critical Value, z: 1.645
Test Statistic, z: 1.032

We can also see that the P-Value is 0.15, much bigger than the significance level of 0.05. Since we fail to reject the null hypothesis, which means there is not sufficient evidence to support the claim that it takes more than 20 minutes to read this section.

Testing a Claim about a Population Mean: σ unknown

Assumptions

1. The sample is a simple random sample.
2. σ is unknown
3. At least one of the following conditions is satisfied: the sampled population is normal or the sample size n > 30.

➤ State H_0 and H_1.
➤ Determine the critical values and the critical regions. The critical values will be t values.
➤ Calculate the value of test statistic: $t = \dfrac{\bar{x} - \mu}{\dfrac{s}{\sqrt{n}}}$.

➤ Determine whether the test statistic falls in the critical region or whether the P-value is larger or smaller than α.
➤ Make a decision about H_0 (reject H_0 if the test statistic falls in the critical region).
➤ Write a final conclusion about the original claim.

Example 1: Test the claim that the average age of girls in Junior Girl Scouts is 10 years old. A simple random sample of 40 girls results in a mean of 9.7 and a standard deviation of 0.6. Use significance level $\alpha = 0.05$.

Solution:
In this example, we have a simple random sample with n>30. The standard deviation s of the sample is known, but the standard deviation σ of the population is unknown. Furthermore, we have sample size n=40, mean of the sample $\bar{x} = 9.7$, and the standard deviation of the sample s=0.6.

Once again, we will analyze the claim by going through all the steps of the hypothesis testing and then we will show how to use Statdisk to solve the problem.

The two opposing statements are:
$\mu = 10$ (claim)
$\mu \neq 10$

The statement that does not contain any kind of equality is called H_1. The other statement is already in the form "=" and therefore it is H_o:
H_1: $\mu \neq 10$
H_o: $\mu = 10$

Based on the direction of H_1, this is an example of a two-tailed test. Since the standard deviation σ of the population is unknown, we use Student t-distribution to find the critical values. Area in the two tails is 0.05 with df = n-1 = 39. Using the Student t-distribution table, we obtain critical values t = -2.023 and t = +2.023. Note that since this is a two tailed test, we must come up with two critical values.

The test statistics is calculated using the formula:

$$t = \frac{\bar{x} - \mu}{\frac{s}{\sqrt{n}}} = \frac{9.7 - 10}{\frac{0.6}{\sqrt{40}}} \approx -3.16$$

Clearly the test statistic falls in the critical region. Therefore, the initial conclusion is that we reject the null hypothesis in favor of the alternative hypothesis. To finish the problem, we need to state our final conclusion in terms of the original claim (μ =10). The final conclusion is that at the significance level 0.05, we have sufficient evidence to reject the claim that the mean age of girls in Junior Girl Scouts is 10 years old.

Here is how we can use Statdisk to solve this problem. This is an example of a two-tailed test. The area in each tail is one half of 0.05 or 0.025. This can also be done in Statdisk by using "Analysis" – "Hypothesis Testing: Mean On-

Sample". Leave the drop down menu as =. Enter the claimed mean as 10, the sample size as 40, the sample mean as 9.7 and the sample standard deviation of 0.6 to get these results:

We can select plot to see the two tails of this test. You can see that the test statistic falls way to the left, in the critical region. As a result, the sample provides sufficient evidence to reject the null hypothesis. Our final conclusion is that the sample provides sufficient evidence to reject the claim that the mean age of girls in Junior Girl Scouts is 10 years old.

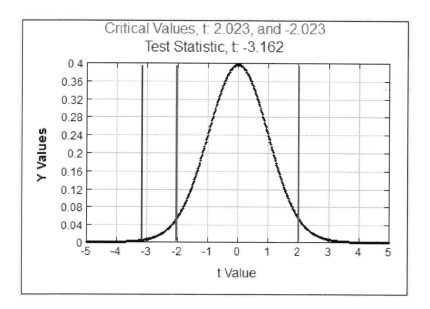

Critical Values, t: 2.023, and -2.023
Test Statistic, t: -3.162

Example 2: Test the claim the new RV models get an average of at least 15 miles to the gallon. In a simple random sample of 35 new RVs, the average miles per gallon was 13.1 with a standard deviation of 0.7. Use significance level $\alpha = 0.05$.

Solution:
We have a simple random sample with n>30. The standard deviation s of the sample is known, but the standard deviation σ of the population is unknown. Furthermore, we have sample size n=35, mean of the sample $\bar{x} = 13.1$, and the standard deviation of the sample s=0.7.

First we will go through all the steps of the hypothesis testing and then we will show how to use Statdisk to analyze the claim.

The two opposing statements are:
$\mu \geq 15$ (claim)
$\mu < 15$

The statement that does not contain any kind of equality is called H_1. We change the other statement to "=" and call it H_o:

$H_1: \mu < 15$
$H_0: \mu = 15$

Based on the direction of H_1, this is an example of a left-tailed test. Since the standard deviation σ of the population is unknown, we use Student t-distribution to find the critical value. Area in one two tail is 0.05 with df = n-1 = 34. Using the Student t-distribution table, we obtain critical value t = -1.691. Note that since this is a left tailed test, we must come up with one negative critical value.

The test statistics is calculated using the formula:

$$t = \frac{\bar{x} - \mu}{\frac{s}{\sqrt{n}}} = \frac{13.1 - 15}{\frac{0.7}{\sqrt{35}}} \approx -16.06$$

The test statistic falls far to the left and well in the critical region. Therefore, the initial conclusion is that we reject the null hypothesis and the statement of equality in favor of the alternative hypothesis.

We now need to address the original claim ($\mu \geq$ 15). The final conclusion is that at the significance level 0.05, we have sufficient evidence to reject the claim that the new RV models get an average of at least 15 miles to the gallon.

Here is how we can use Statdisk to go through the steps pf hypothesis testing. This is an example of a left-tailed test. The area in the tail is 0.05. To use Statdisk, we can choose the "Analysis" – "Hypothesis Test" – "Mean One-Sample". From the drop down menu we select "Pop Mean > or = Claimed Mean" and enter the claimed mean of 15 with the sample size of 35, sample mean of 13.1 and sample standard deviation of 0.7.

```
Hypothesis Testing: One Mean

3) Pop. Mean > or = Claimed Mean

Significance:        0.05           Claim:      μ > or =  μ(hyp)
Claimed Mean:        15
                                    t Test
Population St Dev:                  Test Statistic, t: -16.0579
(if known)                          Critical t:        -1.6909
                                    P-Value:            0.0000
Sample Size, n:      35
                                    90% Confidence interval:
Sample Mean:         13.1           12.89993 <  μ < 13.30007

Sample St Dev, s:    .7
                                    Reject the Null Hypothesis
   Evaluate                         Sample provides evidence to
                                    reject the claim
   Plot

   Help ?
                                               Print      Copy
```

Notice the results again indicate we should reject the null hypothesis. We can also see the values for the Test Statistics, Critical t, P-value and Confidence interval. If we look at the plot we will see that this is a left tailed test and that the test statistics falls outside in the left critical region or tail.

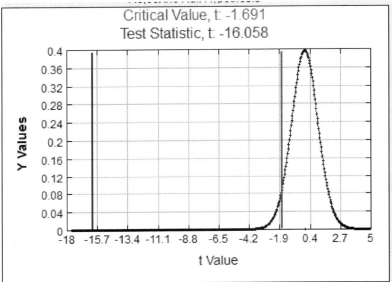

Since we reject H_0, our final conclusion is that there is sufficient evidence to reject the claim that the new RV models get at least 15 miles to the gallon.

In both of the prior examples the Student t-distribution was used rather than the normal distribution. This is due to the assumptions for the test. The normal distribution requires the population standard deviation for the calculation of the test statistic while the t-distribution does not require the value of σ for the test statistic.

Explorations

Social Justice as a Team:

1. Is the cost of educating a 5th grader in a public school in a low income district (bottom 25%) less than the cost to educate an average 5th grader in a public school in a high income district (top 25%)? Support your conclusion. How might Respect be important when setting school budgets?
2. How does the amount given in food stamps to an average family of 4 compare to the amount an average family of 4 spends per week on groceries? Support your conclusion. What values are important to consider when making public policies?
3. Choose a city. Is the amount paid for a 2 bedroom, one bath home for Section 8 housing more than the average paid for a 2 bedroom, one bath home in the same community that is privately rented? Support your conclusion. What values are important to consider when making public policies?

Values and Critical Thinking for problem solving:

1. Is the percent of people in the US considered hungry over 25%? What information did you use to make your conclusion? Can you find any problems with the way this question is phrased? What would be a question that would have more integrity and respect for this important study?

2. Find an article that makes a conclusion to a hypothesis that you believe is incorrect. Explain the reason you think the conclusion, study, or findings are wrong or invalid and what you would have done differently to correct them. What values, such as respect, are neglected when incorrect information is publicized?

Social Justice in the News:

1. Find an article with a conclusion or data or exploration that offers a vehicle or tool that could be used to help understand or improve social conditions in our present world. Explain why you chose that particular article and what values are important to consider.

2. Find a particular collection, representation, or publication of data, where you can determine a group or person who appears to benefit and/or who appears to suffer. Whose values may be implicitly represented or excluded?

Writing Across the Curriculum:

1. How do you determine whether to use the normal distribution or the Student t-distribution for a test of hypothesis?
2. Make up or find four different claims that can be tested by a test of hypothesis. Construct the four different sets of hypothesis. Make up an initial conclusion for each set. Write the final conclusion that goes with the hypotheses and initial conclusions you created.

Chapter 8: Correlation and Regression

Linear correlation and regression are used to analyze the relationship between two quantitative variables provided that relationship can be modeled with a straight line.

Linear Correlation

There is a <u>correlation</u> between x and y if as x increases, there is a consistent shift in the values of y. There is no correlation if as x increases there is no consistent shift in the values of y.

A correlation is <u>linear</u> if the ordered pairs (x, y) follow a line-like pattern. It is called a <u>perfect linear correlation</u> if all the points fall exactly on the line.

Correlation is <u>positive</u> if y increases as x increases. It is said to be <u>negative</u> if y decreases as x increases.

<u>The coefficient of linear correlation, r,</u> is a measure of the strength of the linear relationship between x and y. We shall use technology to approximate r. The values of r will always fall between -1 and 1 inclusive. The value of r needs to exceed the critical value for the significance level of the test

in order for the regression equation to be used for prediction and to consider the variables to have a linear relationship.

Correlation Coefficient:
1. $-1 \leq r \leq 1$
2. $r = -1$ means a perfect negative linear correlation
3. $r = 1$ means a perfect positive linear correlation
4. r closer to zero means a weak or no linear correlation
5. Typically we round off r to the nearest hundredth

Most software will calculate the linear correlation coefficient at the same time as calculating the regression equation. You can then review the linear correlation coefficient to determine whether the regression equation is useful or not. See the example at the end of this section.

Linear Regression, Variation, and Prediction Intervals

Suppose there is a linear relationship between x and y. The method of least squares is used to find the equation of the line that best describes this relationship. The line is called the line of regression and can be used to predict the value of y for a given value of x.

The *line of regression* might use slightly different symbols but will look like: $y = b_0 + b_1x$, where b_0 is the y-intercept and b_1 is the slope.

Many software programs will calculate as well as plot the line of regression and give the correlation coefficient. However, it is up to you to determine whether linear regression exists and the regression equation should be used for making predications. If there does not appear to be a linear relationship, then the mean of all y values is the best predicated y value for any given x. Even if the software provides numbers that indicate a linear relationship, the graph should be verified to make sure a linear relationship is in fact visible.

Example: In a study at Saint Leo University, the practice test scores and actual test scores in an Introduction to Statistics class were collected and are given below. Find the best predicted test score based on a practice quiz score of 75%

Practice	93	80	95	72	0	31	66	64	0	0	56	0	54
test	81	61	100	83	77	78	80	80	52	47	84	41	47

0	0	77	92	89	92	0	85	58	87	0
48	61	83	72	97	92	39	88	55	92	67

The analysis can be done using statistical software, such as Statdisk, entering the data in to the columns and then selecting Analysis – Correlation and Regression" then selecting the two appropriate columns before choosing "Evaluate".

The correlation coefficient is given as r=0.7323811 and this is above the critical value of .404386 that is needed to support linear correlation, so that means the data does have a linear relationship so the equation will be useful for making the predication. The equation is given as Y= b0 + b1x where b0 is 53.62997 and b1 is .3508655 for a regression equation of Y=53.62997+.3508655x. This rounds to Y=53.63+.35x and we can then predict the test value for a practice quiz value of 75 as Y=53.63+.35(75) = 53.63+26.25 = 79.88 or a test grade of 80%. However, we should also select "plot" just to be sure the date roughly follows the direction of the line.

In the next graph, you can see that the points do not fall on the line or even very close to the line, but they do follow the pattern of the line in general.

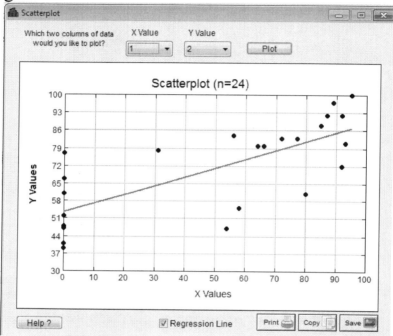

Example: In a recent study, student weights were collected with their test scores. Find the best predicted value of a student test score who weighs 137 pounds.

The weights test scores, and linear regression analysis is as follows:

R...	1	2
1	144	81
2	206	61
3	153	100
4	143	83
5	177	77
6	165	78
7	132	80
8	124	80
9	127	52
10	119	47
11	136	84
12	157	41
13	153	47
14	149	48
15	182	61
16	147	83
17	196	72
18	173	97
19	158	92
20	149	39
21	136	88
22	162	55
23	127	92
24	116	67

Correlation and Regression

Significance: 0.05

Select the columns to be used for the x and y variables.

x variable column: 1

y variable column: 2

Evaluate

Plot

```
Sample size, n:          24
Degrees of freedom:      22

Correlation Results:
Correlation coeff, r:   -0.0295728
Critical r:             ±0.404386
P-value (two-tailed):   0.89089

Fail to Reject the Null Hypothesis
Sample does not provide enough evidence to
support a linear correlation

Regression Results:
Y= b0 + b1x:
Y Intercept, b0:        74.58331
Slope, b1:              -0.0234094

Total Variation:        7930.958
Explained Variation:    6.936007
Unexplained Variation:  7924.022
Standard Error:         18.97848
Coeff of Det, R^2:      0.0008745
```

Notice that the correlation coefficient is -.0295728 and this is not outside of the critical values so that means there is no linear relationship between student weight and their performance on a Statistics test in this study. That means we should not use the regression equation that the software provided, because it is not a good predictor. In this case, the best predictor is the mean of the given scores so we would find the mean of the second column and see that the best predicted test score is 71% regardless of the student's weight.

Explorations

Team Activities:

1. Choose a prediction that your team can answer using linear regression and then

answer it. Show the data that you used and the process you used to arrive at your result.

2. Construct a set of data that gives the result that linear regression is a good tool to use to make predictions but that the graph of the data clearly indicate linear regression is not the best model.

Values and Critical Thinking for problem solving:

1. Find a study that uses linear regression. What is the purpose of the study? What is the key question the author is attempting to answer? What is the most important information? What is the main inference? What key concepts do we need to understand? What assumption is underlying the author's thinking? What are the implications of the study? Who sponsored the study? What is the main point of view of the author? Who could benefit or be hurt by the study?

2. Critical thinking can be used to find faulty assumptions or conclusions. Find a study that uses linear regression where the either the assumptions or conclusions could be wrong or problematic. Describe the faulty logic in the study. What are some of the first steps in setting up a valid research study that might have helped this researcher to

maintain integrity and excellence within the study?

Social Justice:

1. Use the critical thinking skill of skepticism to find an article where causation is indicated but only correlation is shown. What are some other possible causes that could have contributed to the result? What individuals or groups stand to gain or lose from the causation that was stated?

In the News:

1. Find an example in the news of non-linear regression and also an example of linear regression and discuss each.
2. Find an article that contains a linear regression equation. Discuss the domain of values that can be used with the equation to make valid predictions. Explain what values should be used for predications with the equation and why.

Writing Across the curriculum:

1. Can you think of any examples of ways that you have used linear regression at your job or in your daily life?

2. Choose three different technology tools, such as Excel, Statdisk, graphing calculator, or online applications that will calculate linear regression. Use each tool for an example and explain the advantages and disadvantages of each.